Other books by Stanley M. Maxwell

Him Big God Day

The Man Who Couldn't Be Killed

The Man Who Lived Twice

Prisoner for Christ

MIRACLES IN UNEXPECTED PLACES STANLEY MAXWELL

Pacific Press®
Publishing Association

Nampa, Idaho | Oshawa, Ontario, Canada
www.pacificpress.com

Cover design by Gerald Lee Monks
Cover design resources from iStockphoto.com
Inside design by Kristin Hansen-Mellish

The author assumes full responsibility for the accuracy of all facts and quotations as cited in this book.

Additional copies of this book may be obtained by calling toll-free 1-800-765-6955 or online at http://www.adventistbookcenter.com.

Library of Congress Cataloging-in-Publication Data
Maxwell, Stanley M., 1958–
  Miracles in unexpected places / Stanley M. Maxwell.
    pages cm
  ISBN 13: 978-0-8163-5018-6 (pbk.)
  ISBN 10: 0-8163-5018-3 (pbk.)
1. Christian life. 2. Miracles. I. Title.
  BV4509.5.M34155 2014
  231.7'3—dc23
                              2013040046

February 2014

Contents

Dedicated to

My family—my mother, my wife, and Roxy and Nigel.

Also dedicated to all the children who've listened to these stories and asked for another.

Behind the Stories

Let's get this perfectly straight: There are miracles and there are miracles and then there are *miracles*. Some miracles are meant to appear miraculous but are tricks of magic in which the hand is quicker than the eye. Some miracles are outright fraudulent—like CGI in superhero movies, for example. Other fraudulent claims can later be explained scientifically, such as spontaneous generation—the scarab beetle doesn't arise spontaneously from a ball of dung, as was once taught, but from eggs laid inside the ball. Then there are events that are inexplicable and unrepeatable and are therefore truly miraculous. These miracles are incredible, unbelievable, fabulous, amazing, and sometimes mysterious.

While admittedly some true miracles, like childbirth, occur regularly, real miracles have a peculiar habit of occurring in unexpected places and at unexpected times. When and where God will intervene miraculously in people's lives is generally unpredictable—but miracles *do* happen, and when they do, it makes for a good story. The title, *Miracles in Unexpected Places,* is intended to reflect that phenomenon.

I believe that God uses miracles to help increase faith in the hearts of His children here on Earth—and perhaps on other worlds as well. I also believe God created human beings because He loves a good story. The stories within these pages are about miracles that have happened to real people. They tell of God's presence in this world today and how He loves and cares for humanity.

I found these stories in my files while searching for the stories to include in *Him Big God Day,* a collection of Sabbath stories. For those of you who've already read *Him Big God Day* and are now reading *Miracles in Unexpected Places,* you need little introduction to the history of Mr. Stan and his stories. But something needs to be written for those who may not have read my earlier books.

When I was a little boy, I wanted to write stories. I remember listening to stories at the dining table at my father's home and collecting stories from the age of five. My father, Dr. C. Mervyn Maxwell, son of "Uncle Arthur" Maxwell, often invited guests and asked them to tell stories at worships around the fire in the living room or while sitting around the dining table on Sabbaths.

After recording stories for *Picnic Family* on WAUS, I went overseas, where Thais and Chinese encouraged me to tell them stories of life in America. God graciously allowed me to travel and live in many countries, including Thailand, Hong Kong, Macau, China, Philippines, Kyrgyzstan, Jordan, Peru, Ecuador, Costa Rica, Trinidad, Uzbekistan, Great Britain, and Austria, where I collected more stories. These stories have been orally tested on primary, junior, and young adult audiences and warmly received in camp meetings, in churches, in schools, at camporees, on cable television, and on radio.

The Chinese have a saying that a tourist sees the flowers while flying by on horseback; in contrast, during my travels, I got off the horse to smell the flowers. As a result, I spent time with people in various countries and cultures, observing them and listening to their stories. I shared these stories with children and with adults in Central Asia, Asia, and North and South America. Upon my return to America, I began telling stories to Americans about the lives of people in Europe, the Middle East, Asia, the Caribbean, and South America.

In *Him Big God Day,* my theme was Sabbath stories. I wanted to show that God honors those who honor His special day. With the miracle stories in this book, I hope to show that miracles are not just a phenomenon of biblical times—God can and still does perform miracles in modern times. These true stories fall into six categories:

The first category is a story where a miracle occurred on the Sabbath day. Yes, I found more Sabbath stories after finishing *Him Big God Day.* The second is where it appears that angels assisted human beings. The third are stories about answers to prayers. The fourth is where events caused the miracle of a change of heart. A fifth might be described as a common, yet mysterious phenomenon that built an individual's faith. For the sixth, I added an allegory.

Several people who need to be thanked for their help in the process of writing these stories are: Dr. Ron du Preez, Dr. Brian Strayer, and my daughter C. Roxanne Maxwell for assisting in editing. Scott Cady, Jerry D. Thomas, Anita Seymour, and others at the Pacific Press®, as well as my father and mother, should all be thanked for their encouragement. My wife, Phemie, who by

Behind the Stories

lovingly fixing meals, by dutifully keeping the household running, and by regularly tending to the children's needs, freed me up to spend time on stories. Most important, I can't forget all the children who've heard me tell stories and asked, "When are your stories going to come out in a book?"

When you read these stories, you might think that one or two of them sound familiar, or you might remember them differently. Names, dates, and sometimes places have occasionally been changed to protect the innocent or ignorant. These stories are based on the oral tradition of storytelling. Memory is fickle, and details sometimes change in the telling. The source for the story may be different, and as any court case will tell you, three witnesses to the same event will each give a slightly different account, but it doesn't make the story any less true. These stories are the way I remember them being told to me.

Stanley M. Maxwell

Chapter 1

Ghost-busting in Thailand

Lee awoke abruptly.

Dreams, two terrible dreams. The first was a mystery, the second, frightening. He tried to focus his eyes on the moonbeams filtering through his split-bamboo hut. His nostrils flared at the smell of the fire smoldering in the middle of the uneven dirt floor. He tossed on his woven mat, trying to sleep. It was useless. Just thinking about his dreams made his heart pound loudly. What could they mean?

Lee pushed himself off his mat and instinctively brushed off his loose clothing. He wore baggy black pants and a brightly embroidered jacket, the traditional attire of Hmong* hill tribes, who live near the Burmese border in northern Thailand. Around his neck hung a pure silver necklace, which all Hmong knew protected them from ghosts that might try to strangle them in their sleep.

He stared at the ghosthouse on the wall. The ghosthouse is a place for a ghost to stay. This one was constructed of paper with a corrugated fringe and many diamond-shaped cutouts decorating the middle. A shelf jutted out below the paper structure. On the shelf rested bowls of food and water from which a ghost could dine. A stick of incense glowed, its sweet smell contrasting with the embers of the fire that heated the hut.

"Don't even touch the ghosthouse," Lee's mother used to warn, "or you'll die."

---

* Hmong is pronounced "mong."

Ghost-busting in Thailand

Have I offended the ghosts? Lee wondered. One could never be sure without first talking to the witch doctor. Only the witch doctor could interpret dreams correctly.

Stepping through the door, Lee ducked under the elephant-grass roof. He chased down his prized hen, snatched it by its legs, and started toward the witch doctor's hut. The bird curled its head upright so as not to see the world upside down. It looked around casually, its body swinging gently with each new step of the worried Hmong.

The witch doctor opened the door slowly to Lee's timid knock. His tall bony body loomed larger than life. The purple daybreak reflected in his glassy eyes. His black hair hung in long strands down to his shoulders. He smiled a toothy grin at Lee. "Do you need my services?"

Lee hesitated. "I need you to talk to the ghosts. I'm afraid. I've had two terrible dreams, and I must know their meanings!"

The witch doctor's eyes passed from Lee to the dangling bird. "What's that?" he asked knowingly. For a fleeting moment Lee was afraid his offering was too small. But he spoke confidently, "A gift for you."

The old man took the offering and set it on the ground. The grateful fowl ran inside the hut. "What were the dreams?"

"In my first dream, my family and I hiked down the mountain to work in the fields. We arrived at the farm together, but when I looked around, my family was gone. I looked everywhere, but I was alone! Then I awoke." Lee wiped sweat off his brow.

"And the second?" the witch doctor prodded.

"In my second dream, I was in a strange field near a village that I've never seen before. A stranger approached me and asked, 'Do you need a house?' Before I could answer, 'No,' he declared, 'I've got the perfect house for you. It's very small. Just big enough for you to sleep in. And I have other homes for your family right next to yours.' " Lee felt faint. "Please ask the ghosts the interpretation."

"I don't have to ask. Many people share these dreams. The meaning is always the same." The witch doctor lit his water pipe. Water inside the bamboo tube gurgled as he sucked on the mouthpiece.

"What do they mean?" Lee begged.

The old man blew a cloud of smoke, remaining silent.

"Tell me!" Lee demanded desperately.

"The meaning of the first dream is uncertain. When you arrive at the fields, you can't find your family. You miss them. This has one of two meanings: either your family will die and you'll miss them, or you'll die and your family will miss you."

"But I know the meaning of the second dream. In that dream you're asked if you want a house. But it's big enough only for you to sleep in. That house is your tomb. This dream says you and your family will die."

Lee's throat went dry. "What do I do now?"

"I suggest you go home and prepare to die." The witch doctor averted his gaze. He had nothing more to say.

Lee's shoulders drooped. His feet grew heavy as he slowly trudged home to report the news. "I'm too young to die. How can I tell my family?"

The Hmong family sat around a low hand-hewn table. His wife, Bee, served rice on a banana leaf with bowls of meat and vegetable soup. Each person used his fingers to pry off a cluster of rice from the pile and then spooned some soup.

Lee swallowed hard. "I had two bad dreams last night." He reached for more rice then drew his hand back nervously. "I asked the witch doctor for the interpretation."

"What did he say?" Bee asked.

"The ghosts are angry. I don't know why. We're going to die!" There. He'd said it!

"Is there something we can do to appease the ghosts?" Lee's wife sounded hopeful. "Maybe they'll change their minds."

"No. The witch doctor said we're to prepare to die."

"I don't want to die!" Bee protested.

"Neither do I," Lee sighed sadly. "But the ghosts say we'll die."

"So we will die." His wife nodded matter-of-factly.

Some days later, Yang, Lee's sister, complained of being hot, although the day was cool. Sweat beaded on her forehead and trickled down her cheeks. Yang was being burned up by an unseen fire. She could only lie motionless and moan. Lee knew the ghosts had struck.

Lee's wife found a branch with dead leaves and tied it to the doorpost. This told the neighbors, "If you visit our family, you might get sick and die!"

Only one man dared visit the hut—Pastor Sae Saeyang, the son of the witch doctor, who had rejected ghosts for Jesus.*

"Is someone sick?" the pastor asked.

"My sister is dying," Lee said. "The ghosts said in dreams that our family will die."

"Do you believe the ghosts?"

Lee nodded. "The ghosts are always right. If they say we die, we die."

"You're right. Ghosts have some power, but Christ is more powerful than ghosts!"

"I don't believe in Christ. I'm a ghost worshiper!"

"If you'll let me take the ghosthouse out of your house, and if you'll become a Christian, your sister will get well. Your family won't die. The ghosts cannot harm a Christian—"

Lee slammed the door in the pastor's face.

Yang's breathing became irregular. Each new breath was a frantic search for more air. And then her breathing stopped.

Lee built a bamboo stretcher for carrying his sister to the village death house. In the death house, a drummer beat out a rhythm and a pipe player blew on his bamboo pipes. Lee's eyes followed the pipe player, who was circling a bamboo column. Lee knew the ritual well—he had seen it countless times before. But today was different. This was his sister.

He glanced at the ghosthouse. *Why do I worship the ghosts? What do they do for me?* he asked himself. *They've killed my sister. They'll kill us all soon!*

The music stopped. Lee tied his sister to the stretcher and splashed sacred red dye on her forehead. *Who will die next?* he wondered. Lee and his friends formed a parade and carried the body away for burial.

Some months later, Lee awoke with a fever. Sweat poured down his forehead, stinging his eyes. His brain felt like burning coals. "I'm sick," he announced.

His wife squatted beside him, wiping his sweat away and crying. He knew he was dying.

Is Christ more powerful than ghosts? I was a fool not to give my sister a chance. His mind reeled with his thoughts. *But I was afraid I'd die if the pastor touched the ghosthouse. Yang might be alive today if I'd listened to the pastor.*

He turned feverish eyes toward his wife. "Do you think Pastor Sae would

---

* Stanley M. Maxwell witnessed this story while working in Thailand. He lived among the Hmong in 1983. Pastor Sae Saeyang was his roommate.

13

come again after what I did?" he asked. "Please ask him to come. Tell him I apologize for slamming the door in his face. He's my only hope!"

"I'll go!" Bee hurriedly obeyed her husband's dying wish.

Pastor Sae's smile faded when he saw how sick Lee had become. "May I do something for you?"

"The ghosts were right. I'm dying."

"Christ can heal you. The ghosts promise you death; Christ promises you life," the pastor encouraged.

"Take the ghosthouse out of my house!" Lee whispered hoarsely.

Pastor Sae's eyes sparkled. "Everyone come around the fire," he ordered.

Everyone moved to the center of the house except Lee, who was too weak. Pastor Sae looked from face to face. "Do you agree to become Christian?"

Everyone nodded solemnly. Lee wondered what the ghosts would do.

Pastor Sae continued. "Let's pray. I know, Jesus, that You're more powerful than ghosts. I thank You for this family who has decided to become Your children today. Bless them. Don't allow the ghosts to kill them. Please live here. Make their home Your home. In Christ's name, Amen."

Pastor Sae got up. He tore the ghosthouse off the wall. The family held each other tightly as the pastor rolled up the ghosthouse and touched the tip to the fire until the paper burst into a blaze. "Ghosts, leave this house!" he called loudly. "You can't live here anymore; this is a *Christian* house now!" Turning, the pastor walked out the door with the flaming ghosthouse in hand and set it on the ground.

Ghosts hate fire, Lee reminded himself.

Pastor Sae reentered the hut. "Do you have anything else that relates to the ghosts here?" he asked, eyeing their necklaces.

The family quickly took off their necklaces and handed them to the pastor. Lee was sure unseen hands would choke out his life. But nothing happened.

The pastor shook the necklaces over the fire and said, "Ghosts, leave these necklaces," and set them beside the ashes of the ghosthouse.

Pastor Sae looked around the hut. "Anything else?"

Bee produced a dirty burlap pouch with two gourds and a bone-shaped stick inside. The pastor waved the bag over the fire. "Ghosts, leave these things." He walked outside and set the bag of gourds beside the necklaces and the ashes of the ghosthouse.

Ghost-busting in Thailand

Pastor Sae asked about the branch.

Lee watched his wife untie the branch of dead leaves from the doorpost. He thought, *This pastor really believes I'll get well.*

Pastor Sae shook the branch over the flames. "Ghosts, I'm going to shake you out of this branch!" He went outside, still shaking the branch, and set it beside the bag of gourds, the necklaces, and the ashes of the ghosthouse.

The family joined him outside, looking at the symbols of ghost protection. Lee gratefully took back the pure silver necklaces. They were valuable. But Pastor Sae kept the worthless branch of dead leaves and the bag of gourds.

The pastor left the hut. Still shaking the branch, he shouted, "Goodbye, ghosts! Christ is more powerful than ghosts!"

Lee's family didn't die. Today, many years later, they are happy Christians, free from the ghosts' power. Lee knows Christ *is* more powerful than ghosts.

Chapter 2

An Unexpected Turn of Events

In March of 1906, Eduardo Forga, a wealthy young Peruvian mining engineer and political activist turned fugitive, followed the governor's advice and hid in a cornfield while soldiers searched his house. He walked by night and hid by day and then boarded a freight train to the port city of Mollendo. Wondering whether he'd ever see his beloved Arequipa again, he headed for London. It was a strange victory for the agents of change in Peru. True, the liberal heads of government hadn't handed Forga over to the priests, but to save his life, they had deported their major weapon. *What lies ahead?* Forga asked himself as he stood at the rails of the deck. The waves crested and crashed methodically against the side of the ship as he lost himself in thought. *How can I help to free Peru from the corrupt clergy if I am in Europe?*

In London, he found refuge in the Regions Beyond Mission, where his stories inspired twenty missionaries to start work with the South American Indians. But Forga was restless, uncertain where God wanted him to be. Should he return to Germany, where he had first found his evangelical fervor? Stopping at a vegetarian restaurant after buying passage to Germany, he sat at a table and ordered. While waiting to be served, he prayed fervently for guidance.

Someone sitting in the restaurant saw the anguish on Forga's face and, thinking it would do him some good, handed him a notice about a series of lectures on the prophecies of Daniel, which piqued Eduardo's curiosity. Checking it over carefully, he saw that the meetings began that very night. As he ate, he wondered, *Is the invitation to these lectures the answer to my prayer?* The only way to know was to attend that evening's lecture.

Canceling his passage to Germany, Forga attended the lecture. As he listened to the speaker, Herbert Lacey, the message reminded him of a little paper he'd once received from Argentina. He recalled reprinting many of its articles and distributing them throughout Peru and its neighboring countries. So here was someone else who thought the same way.

Forga eagerly attended the rest of the series. It was the first time he'd ever come face to face with Seventh-day Adventists. He was happy to attend a church that espoused vegetarianism and a health message.

An older man took an interest in Forga. "Hello, Brother Eduardo, I'm David Lacey." He extended his hand and they shook vigorously. "I think you're very interested in what my son is teaching."

"Herbert Lacey is your son?" Forga replied.

"Yes," David Lacey said proudly.

"It's an honor to meet you, Brother Lacey."

After he had talked awhile and listened to Forga's faltering English, David Lacey discovered that Eduardo was a young fugitive from Peru. Upon hearing this, he invited him to dine with them and board at his home. "We can study more about the Bible together," he suggested.

"Yes, I would like that," Forga replied. "I need to learn more. What better chance than in your house, yes?"

"Of course." David Lacey smiled.

Forga arrived at the Lacey home at the designated time. Soon everyone was called to the table to eat. It was then that he met the evangelist's daughter, Marguerite. As he sat at the Lacey table, he couldn't help observing her grace and beauty. Forga responded with the charm common among elite educated Latin families.

When, after the meal, arrangements were made for him to stay in their home, Forga was delighted. While he liked nothing better than to study the Bible with Brother David, it also afforded him a bonus—the opportunity to get better acquainted with pretty Miss Lacey.

The longer he spent boarding at the Laceys', the more he noticed Marguerite. There was something about her that seemed to him to surpass all the other women he'd ever met. Eventually, he decided to tell her of his admiration, but

English wasn't his best language. If only she could speak German, French, or Spanish—he was fluent in all three. French was the language of love—and Spanish the one of chivalry and romance, but English! Why did Marguerite have to speak such a clumsy language as English?

One day, he chanced to meet Miss Lacey alone. *Perhaps this is my opportunity to express my admiration,* he thought. But what should he say? Choosing to be direct but not being proficient in English, he blurted out, "You're going to be my wife!"

Turning several shades of red, Miss Lacey snapped, "I already have someone." With that, she marched out of the room. *How dare he? How can he think I'd want to be his wife? The very idea!*

Following that exchange, tension flooded the home. Miss Lacey avoided the boarder as best she could, but mealtimes were unpleasant. She felt increasingly uncomfortable in Eduardo's presence. Soon the atmosphere was unbearable for all.

"Your attraction to Marguerite has made your continuing to stay here awkward. I think, under the circumstances, it's best for you to find boarding elsewhere," the Laceys told Eduardo one day.

Perhaps because of cultural differences and language difficulties, Forga was taken off guard. The rejection hurt him deeply. First, his own family didn't understand his Protestant ideas; then his friend, the governor, had persuaded him to leave his homeland; and now the woman with whom he wanted to share his life had spurned him, and her family was sending him away. How could he leave? He had met his destiny! While he was aware that she hadn't accepted his proposal immediately, he'd merely assumed that, in time, Marguerite would change her mind. *He was the man for her. Who could be better? No one!* He'd been as certain of that fact as he was that the sun would rise in the morning.

Was his assumption incorrect? The Laceys obviously thought so. Where was he to go? What was he to do? He was too much of a gentleman to insist he stay, but what was to become of him? Hastily he packed and, after offering charming goodbyes to the Laceys, headed out into the unknown.

Soon he found himself aimlessly strolling down the streets of London, discouraged. *Has God forsaken me? Is there even a God?* he asked himself.

Almost in answer to his questions, a group of people befriended him. When they learned he was looking for a place to board, they suggested he join them. "Come to our meetings."

An Unexpected Turn of Events

Eduardo agreed and learned that his new friends were spiritualists. It seemed fitting to him to learn what they taught. If there was no God—and if his life were any example, it appeared to be true—the next question to ask was, Is there life after death? Maybe they could divine his future. Besides, it became obvious that the spiritualists were looking out for the fugitive from Peru.

Before too long, he had thrown all his energies into their arena. In turn, they helped him meet an attractive young woman from among them. God, Protestantism, Adventism, his Bible studies, and the charming Miss Lacey were all forgotten.

Eduardo was considering marrying his new girlfriend when a letter found its way to his door. Anxiously, he opened it.

It was from Marguerite!

In it she explained that she'd been thinking a lot after he'd left. It seemed she could see more clearly when he was out of the picture. She couldn't forget the Peruvian gentleman who'd been the first to treat her like the lady she'd forgotten that she was. She realized that she was selling herself short by continuing a relationship with a young man who didn't believe in God as she did. At first she'd thought that he'd change, but he hadn't. She really wanted a husband who believed as she did—but she couldn't find one. Then she remembered the fine gentleman from Peru who'd always treated her as befitted a lady. She'd been thinking a lot about him recently and wondered if he could ever forgive her for the way she'd treated him. She was willing to be his wife if he'd have her.

She was willing to be his wife.

Could it be possible? It was too good to be true!

Miss Marguerite Lacey wanted to marry him! The pretty young woman whose discomfort at his presence had forced him to end his stay as a boarder in the Lacey home now wanted to marry him. What an unexpected turn of events! Could it be true? He reread the letter again just to make sure. Yes, indeed, it was!

Eduardo realized that he'd been foolish to become involved with a girl who didn't believe as he did. Both he and Marguerite had been fooling themselves. They had let their need to be loved get in the way of what really mattered to them—obeying God. Marguerite's offer changed all that. Now they could both live with someone who shared the same ideas about God and the Bible. Besides, Eduardo was in love with her—and now he could be with her every day!

To make a long story short, Eduardo parted with his spiritualist friends as amicably as possible, ended the relationship with his spiritualist fiancée, and soon married his true love, Marguerite.

And that was how a wealthy young Peruvian mining engineer and fugitive became a relative of a prolific American author known to many as Sister White. You see, Marguerite Lacey was the sister of Willy White's wife, and Willy was the younger son of Ellen G. White.

Chapter 3

"You Can't Kill Me!"

Mr. Wong was an unusual man.*

Mr. Wong lived in China, you see, and most Chinese are fairly reserved. They don't freely express their feelings—not to friends and especially not to strangers.

Then, too, Mr. Wong lived in China during the Cultural Revolution, a time when most Chinese people went to great lengths to keep their feelings to themselves. This was a time, after all, when talk about anyone other than Party Chairman Mao Zedong could result in a prison term—or even a bullet to the head.

In spite of all this, Mr. Wong greeted everyone he met with a warm smile and a question, "Do you know my Friend Jesus?" He didn't worry about being reported to the authorities. He just wanted everyone to have a chance to meet his Friend.

One day, some youths with red armbands visited Mr. Wong. "We hear you talk about Jesus," they snapped.

"Yes, I do," Mr. Wong replied, even though he knew them to be members of the notorious Red Guard. Red Guards often went for days with hardly a bite of food or a wink of sleep—all for a misguided love, almost worship, of Chairman Mao. (To be sure, their zeal was sometimes also enhanced by their desire to clear black marks from their own dossiers, dossiers tarnished by being descendants of a Kuomintang party member, a capitalist, or intellectual parents.)

---

* Though this is a true story (verified by five sources), dates and names—including place names—have been changed.

"Jesus is my best Friend," continued Mr. Wong. "He can be your Friend too."

"You're proselytizing!" shouted the Red Guards. "Proselytizing is illegal! Religion is the opiate of the people. Liberate yourself from this feudalist nonsense and come into step with New China. Follow the sayings in the little Red Book of our Great Helmsman, Mao Zedong."

"I cannot stop talking about my Friend, if that's what you mean," Mr. Wong calmly replied. He knew that the Red Guards—many of them not yet middle-school students—were caught up in a cause they didn't fully understand. They were only parroting the slogans they'd been taught. Many were giddy with the power they gained by using Mao's sayings.

"*Yo gwideen!* We have a law!" barked the Red Guards.

"I know the law."

"Take him to prison!"

"I'm ready." Mr. Wong picked up his case containing his few belongings— the case he'd packed for just this event. "Take me!"

One of the Red Guards crammed a paper dunce cap on Mr. Wong's head, while another forced Mr. Wong's head down as he walked the dusty streets. All this was to show his "guilt" and submission to the will of the people. The Red Guards then formed a procession and marched Mr. Wong to the city's prison, chanting his crimes to the masses passing by on bicycles. Word of his arrest had spread widely by the time they reached their destination.

If the Red Guards thought placing Mr. Wong behind bars would silence him, they were mistaken. In prison, many inmates were willing to talk with him about his Friend.

"You know why you're in prison!" the guards would shout at him. "Why do you still break China's law?"

"I love China, but I can't stop talking about my Friend," Mr. Wong would reply. "Lonely prisoners need to know Jesus."

"Listen to us," the guards would reply. "We're your friends. Don't make us have to throw you into a stricter prison."

Mr. Wong smiled. "I'll talk about Jesus anywhere."

The guards transferred Mr. Wong to a stricter prison as they'd threatened. But soon he was talking with yet another group of prisoners about Jesus. As a result, Mr. Wong was transferred to the Qinghai Hard Labor Camp—one of the

"You Can't Kill Me!"

harshest labor camps in China at the time. Many were sent, but few returned.

Qinghai is a flat and barren land near Tibet. The air there is thin; the climate, harsh. Besides the usual afflictions of hard work and scant food, prisoners often suffered from exposure, altitude sickness, and dysentery. As a result, many of them died. If those conditions didn't kill, some, to stave off starvation, ate the grass, which was toxic, and they died.

When Mr. Wong arrived in Qinghai, two of the guards ordered him to stop talking about Jesus.

Mr. Wong politely refused.

"Do you know what we'll do to you if you don't quit?"

"You can't kill me!" Mr. Wong responded. He knew his words sounded brash, but a deep confidence in God seemed to assure him that what he had said was actually true.

The guards angrily bound him and beat him. Determined to stop his witnessing once and for all, they led him outside on a bitter snowy night, wrapped his arms and legs together so tightly he could scarcely breath, tied him to a post, and left him alone to die in the cold—at nearly thirty-five degrees below zero.

But the guards forgot that Mr. Wong was not alone. He could pray to his Friend.

And as he prayed, he sensed a presence—an unseen someone who came to him, untied his ropes, then left. The ropes were loose! Mr. Wong was free.

When morning came, however, he faced a new problem. Freed from his bonds, he'd been able to exercise and stay warm. But if the guards found him unbound, they might accuse his friends of sneaking out to untie him. Mr. Wong was glad to be alive, but he didn't want to unwittingly cause other prisoners to be tortured or killed because of him.

So he attempted to tie himself back up. Retying his ankles was easy enough, but how was he to bind his own wrists?

"Lord," he prayed, "You sent my guardian angel to untie me; now, please, tie me up again!"

Mr. Wong felt the ropes tighten around his hands. Once again he was lashed to the post and none too soon. He could already hear the guards approaching.

The guards were, of course, dumbfounded to see Mr. Wong still alive. Muttering to themselves, they untied his ankles. They muttered even more when they tried to untie his hands. The knot at his wrists was so tight that it took the guards half an hour to get it loose. After seeing how long it took the guards to untie the knot, Mr. Wong couldn't help thinking to himself that either his angel didn't know his own strength, or he had a tremendous sense of humor.

Wonderfully sustained by this experience in God's protecting grace, Mr. Wong went right back to asking the prisoners if they knew his Friend Jesus.

The story of how Mr. Wong survived the night spread among both prisoners and guards. One day, a general of the Chinese Liberation Army was so impressed with what he'd heard that he rode on horseback to the labor camp to meet Mr. Wong. After Mr. Wong came out to see the general, the general honored the prisoner by dismounting his horse and standing face to face with Mr. Wong, and shook hands with him. The general then mounted his horse and galloped off.

For a while after that encounter, Mr. Wong was free from extreme persecution, but a few years later the guards became incensed again. Three were assigned to force him to give up his faith in Jesus. All of the prisoners were summoned to watch a reenactment of some late Ch'ing Dynasty torture.

Tying Mr. Wong's hands behind his back, the guards suspended him from the ceiling and then hung a millstone from his neck. After that they began whacking his face as hard as they could until they grew tired. "Are you going to quit talking this Jesus nonsense?" one of the guards asked him after several hours of slapping Mr. Wong.

Mr. Wong was in great pain. He even thought he might have to give in—but not today. Tomorrow, maybe, but for the sake of his Friend, he wouldn't give in today.

"I cannot stop talking about my Friend, Jesus."

The guards continued the torture. They continued asking the same question. Though severely tormented and tempted to give in, Mr. Wong continued to give the same answer. After *seventeen days* of this torture, the guards took him down and threw him on the trash heap outside the camp. They thought he was dead.

But after a while Mr. Wong regained consciousness and found himself atop a pile of dead bodies, the bodies of prisoners who hadn't been so blessed as he. His skin, which had formed scabs during his ordeal, was healed. The scabs flaked off. No scars remained. The pain in his arms and back vanished. Mr.

"You Can't Kill Me!"

Wong thanked his Friend Jesus for healing him; then he returned to the camp.

He now found it easy to form a group of prisoners to whom he could talk about his Friend.

As the years rolled by, Mr. Wong—now known as "the man who couldn't be killed"—continued to talk to other prisoners about Jesus. The guards let him do this; what choice did they have? Finally, in 1979, Mr. Wong was released from the Qinghai Hard Labor Camp.

Today, Mr. Wong is still a very unusual man. Many Chinese people, you see, think that the Cultural Revolution wasted ten or twenty years of their lives, but not Mr. Wong. That's because he has a collection of letters—letters from some of the other survivors of the Qinghai Hard Labor Camp, telling how his experience in prison inspired them to believe that his Real God exists. They thank him for talking about his Friend Jesus.

And that is why, if you were to meet Mr. Wong (who, at the time of this writing, is over eighty years old, but looks and acts like a much younger man), he'd smile, and he'd ask you, "Do you know my Friend Jesus?"

For Mr. Wong knows who it is that made him such an unusual man.

You can read more of Mr. Wong's story in *The Man Who Couldn't Be Killed* (Nampa, Idaho: Pacific Press®, 1998).

Chapter 4

An Ambush and a Prayer

Day after day Nguyen Minh Linh* carefully plotted the fulfillment of his dream. He longed to escape!

Linh lived in North Vietnam during the French occupation. The French Loyalists had suffered heavy losses fighting the Communists and were pulling out. Linh knew he couldn't live in North Vietnam if the Communists won. He wanted to live free.

Rumor whispered that the French Loyalists fared better in South Vietnam, so he decided to flee to Saigon. He started on the long walk south down the dusty roads leading to freedom. The route was riddled with Communist roadblocks and Loyalist checkpoints.

Linh feared he might be stopped and sent back, so he didn't walk on the road but threaded his way through the jungle on a ridge along the roadside. Before stepping into the jungle, he'd taken off his shoes. He'd hoped his footfall would be light and therefore less detectable.

As he walked stealthily through the woods, he saw a movement in the brush. Thinking it might be an animal that he could catch for food, he stopped. Suddenly, from behind thick foliage, a soldier faced him. Linh turned to run, but another soldier jumped down from a branch. Linh tried to escape in another direction but found himself surrounded.

---

* Nguyen Minh Linh (a pseudonym) told me this story in 1985, ten years after Saigon fell, when I was a clothing distributor in a Vietnamese refugee camp in Thailand.

An Ambush and a Prayer

"Ambushed!" He cursed under his breath.

How'd he been so foolish? Now he was trapped. Should he fight or surrender? Now began a frustrating guessing game. He must determine which side they were on without revealing which side he was on. If they were Communists he couldn't say he was a French Loyalist. Then, too, his captors might not be soldiers at all, but thugs and thieves clad in army uniform as disguise.

Linh knew one wrong word could be his last. His speech would betray him even in his choice of pronouns. Respectful pronouns would label him a Loyalist, vernacular ones a Communist. Choices! His head spun.

"Why are you here? Where are you going?" One of the men asked him.

Linh mumbled something so garbled he couldn't understand it himself. Before he could blink he felt himself handcuffed to one of the men. "You're a spy!"

They escorted him off the jungle ridge to the road and half-dragged and half-pushed him to an old French government building. There they prodded him downstairs and threw him into a cell.

When his eyes adjusted to the dim light, Linh surveyed his new surroundings. He counted nineteen other inmates. The floor was damp. Healthy rats rummaged for scraps. One sniffed near Linh's foot. He tried stomping on the pesky rodent but missed.

The creature scurried out of reach down a hole.

"You're all accused of spying," the voice of a guard announced from the cell's trap-door window. "You're too dangerous to live. You'll be shot at 0:00 hours tonight."

In desperation, Linh decided to pray. "Lord, I don't know if You exist or not, but I need You now! Please, get me out of here—and if You're going to do it, make it fast. I have only until midnight to live!"

A guard brought in bowls of soup for the prisoners. It tasted more like water than soup, but Linh found a few grains of rice and a chunk of tough fibrous yam at the bottom of his bowl.

Suddenly, the guard looked Linh straight in the eye and pointed right at him. "You! Are you a French Loyalist?"

Instinct demanded he say No, but a voice in the back of his head commanded him to say, "Yes!" He wanted to kick himself for saying it. If the guard were a Communist sympathizer, Linh would be in deep trouble; and if the guard were a French Loyalist, he probably wouldn't believe Linh anyway. He held his breath and stared back into the guard's eyes.

"Come with me," the guard finally said.

Linh wondered what new trouble he was in now. The guard took him outside to his army truck. "Jump in."

Linh obeyed. He guessed he'd be executed immediately for committing some offense. But if he refused to get in, he might guarantee his premature demise, so he gave his host a broad smile as he hopped into the truck.

The two drove in silence through town. Neither seemed to know what to say. Eventually, the guard pulled his truck up in front of a wooden house and got out. He motioned for Linh to follow. The men kicked off their shoes before entering, then sat cross-legged on the mat-covered floor.

The guard's wife appeared, wearing an attractive sky-blue *ao-dai*. Her fine-featured face had soft skin. She set out bowls of rice for them on the floor. Then she gracefully left the room, to return with dishes of dried fish, boiled shrimp, fried sweet-and-sour pork, and spring rolls. She disappeared again into another room.

Linh had never eaten such good food. He wondered if this was a farewell feast served to French Loyalists as last rites. But why was only he invited? His host said nothing. The guard chewed noisily as he scraped his chopsticks against his bowl.

Suddenly, his host stood up. "Let's go," he said.

Linh got up.

"Follow me." The guard led the way back to the army truck. Linh's heartbeat quickened. The uncertainty needled his nerves. "You can sit up front with me." The guard hopped in and Linh climbed in on the passenger's side. Soon they were back on the road toward his cell.

Midnight was fast approaching and time seemed tyrannically short.

The guard parked in front of the old French government building, and the two got out and returned to the cell.

"Come out single file!" The guard yelled to the inmates. Other guards helped keep the prisoners in line and marched them outside. "Climb into the back of that army truck," they ordered.

The guard who had befriended Linh said to him, "You can ride up front with me." Linh was only too happy to oblige.

An Ambush and a Prayer

Linh sat lost in thought, oblivious to his surroundings. He scarcely noticed as the truck drove away from the lights of the town and careened through monotonous rows of moonlit rice paddies. Linh could only think about himself and the nineteen men riding behind him. The darkness in his mind deepened, and the jungle beyond the windshield matched his mood.

Suddenly, they stopped. "Everyone out!" the guard ordered. Linh heard rushing water and smelled the fresh dampness of a tropical river.

"All right, line up!" The guard yelled. "Face the river and don't move."

Linh started to queue up, but the guard stopped him. "You stay here with me." Why was he singled out? Did the guard plan to shoot him elsewhere? If he had to die, Linh wanted to get it over with immediately.

Gunshots interrupted Linh's self-pity. The guard serially shot the nineteen accused spies in the back of the head. Their bodies fell face forward into the river.

"Get back in the truck."

Linh did as he was told. The guard joined him.

If the guard had any emotion about the night's activities, he kept it to himself. Linh wondered, *What happens next? Why hasn't the guard killed me already?*

"Were you going to Saigon?" the guard blurted out.

"Yes." Linh answered without hesitating.

"Nice place."

"Is it? I've never been there."

"I've been there once or twice. Everything's great—the food, the people and the opportunities. You'll love Saigon!"

Linh forgot he was riding with his captor. Thinking about Saigon helped him forget the corpses bobbing down the river. The guard seemed almost human.

The guard drove farther south. Suddenly he stopped. "This is as far as I can take you."

"And now what?" Linh asked, thinking that now he'd be shot.

"You have a second life now." The guard paused and then added thoughtfully, "What are you going to do with it?" He gave Linh a friendly smile.

Linh could hardly believe his ears. He remembered his prayer in the cell. Was God really looking after him?

"I'm free?"

"Yes."

"I can go now?"

The guard pointed south, "That's the road to Saigon. Take it and you'll get there safely. There are no more checkpoints." The two parted in opposite directions. Joyfully, Linh set out toward Saigon to live the second life granted him by a prayer.

Time passed and Linh forgot about his prayer in that crowded, dank cell. Even in Saigon, his second life was a struggle. The French government left the city and a Nationalist government took over. North Vietnam fought South Vietnam and the Americans supported Saigon. But the Americans, like the French, fared badly against the Vietcong's psychological warfare. In 1975, the Americans left, and the city fell to the Communists.

Linh fled Communism a second time. After bribing officials with gold and fishermen with still more gold, he escaped by sea, crowded into a tiny fishing boat where he braved storms and pirates en route to Thailand.

Linh forgot God, but God did not forget him. In a Thai refugee camp, he heard a sermon about a second life in Jesus. Linh's mind flashed back to his prayer in the cell. He remembered the guard who granted him a second life. There and then, he thanked God and became a Christian.

Today Nguyen Minh Linh resides in the United States. He'll never forget the night he was ambushed and the prayer that led to his second life en route to Saigon; and he remembers the sermon in the refugee camp that led him to become born anew in Jesus Christ.

Chapter 5

The Book Under the Pillow

People in Thailand are a very happy-go-lucky lot. They're full of smiles and enjoy living in the present moment of each day. But one thing frightens them terribly—ghosts. Just the mention of the word *ghost* brings shudders up and down their spines.

Noi* lived in fear every night. She slept in a teak house in a small village surrounded by rice patties. Every night a ghost would walk in through her front door, stand by her bed, and talk to her. Though the ghost's conversation was entertaining, Noi didn't want it to visit her anymore, so she decided to go for help. Noi crossed the village to the pastor's house.

The front door of a Thai's house is always open because the Thai people love to talk with their neighbors. Noi walked to the front door and stood at the entrance.

Pastor Lek looked up to see a woman standing at his doorway. She looked troubled, so he invited her to enter.†

"Good health, pastor." Noi placed the palms of her hands together in a *wai,* a symbol of greeting and respect, which, to an untrained eye, looks like praying hands. Noi smiled gracefully and nodded her head in a way that showed not only respect but that she recognized his importance.

---

* Noi and Lek are extremely common Thai nicknames; they both mean "small" or "little." They are usually used as terms of endearment.

† This is a true story told to me about six years ago by a Thai pastor who was working in Bangkok, Thailand.

"Good health," the pastor replied, returning Noi's wai.

"I have a little problem," Noi smiled, but her eyes looked worried. "Will you help me?"

Mai Pen Rai [No problem]." The pastor smiled warmly, "I'll try my best. What's the problem?"

"A ghost comes to my house every night and talks to me," Noi said, "I don't want him to visit me anymore!"

"There's no need to be afraid of ghosts," the pastor assured Noi. "Jesus is stronger than all the ghosts in the world." Pastor Lek pulled down a Bible from his bookshelf. "Take this book, and the ghost will never visit your house again."

"Thank you very much!" Noi gratefully grasped the Bible and hugged it close to her heart as if it were a charm. "Good luck!" she said as she turned to leave the pastor's house.

"Good luck!" Pastor Lek called after her.

As soon as Noi got back into her house, she placed the book under her pillow.

That night when Noi lay on her teak bed, the ghost came to her door, but he didn't come in. "Noi!" The ghost called from the door. "There's a book under your pillow. Throw it out the window, and I'll come and talk to you."

Noi didn't move.

The ghost got angry and yelled, "Throw that book out the window!"

Noi kept the book under her pillow and ignored the ghost's ranting. Eventually, the ghost left, and Noi got a good night's sleep.

The next night, the ghost came again, but this time he was a little more cross than he'd been the night before. He stopped at the door and demanded, "Noi, throw that book out the window, and I'll come in and talk to you like we did in the good old days."

Noi disobeyed the ghost again. The ghost shouted louder and louder, "Noi throw the book out the window!" But when the ghost saw she wasn't responsive, it left and Noi got another good night's sleep.

On the third night, the ghost again appeared at her door, but he was even more demanding than he'd been on the second night. He reiterated his demand, "Noi! Throw out that book under your pillow, and I'll come in and talk with you."

Noi did nothing of the kind. To her surprise, she saw the ghost shrink

The Book Under the Pillow

smaller and smaller until he was so small that she could barely see him at all. Then he vanished. Noi got her third good night's sleep. On the fourth night, the ghost didn't return and Noi slept peacefully.

When Noi awoke in the morning, she was so happy that the ghost hadn't visited her. She grabbed the Bible and ran all the way to Pastor Lek's house. Noi stood at the entry all out of breath. When the pastor noticed her, she gave him a wai. Pastor Lek returned the gesture and invited her in.

"The ghost doesn't visit my house anymore," Noi exclaimed excitedly. "Thank you so much for your help. Oh, I won't be needing this anymore." Smiling graciously, Noi handed his Bible back to him. Somewhat surprised, but happy for Noi, Pastor Lek took it and Noi left.

That night when Noi went to bed, the ghost came back to her door. It looked monstrous compared to the time before, when he'd shrunk into nothingness. Noi wished she had Pastor Lek's magic book under her pillow for protection. She felt foolish for returning it so quickly. She hoped the ghost thought she still had the book.

But her hopes were dashed. The ghost didn't stand at the door as before. This time he barged right it and stood by her bed, engaging her in conversation against her will. The ghost talked to her all night, not taking his leave until the sunrise shattered the darkness.

After the ghost left, Noi was exhausted. Eventually, she dragged her body out of bed and almost stumbled as she headed in the direction of Pastor Lek's house.

When she saw the pastor, she said, "Pastor Lek, I need that magic book again. The ghost returned last night. As long as I have the magic book, he won't bother me."

"What did you do with the book?" Pastor Lek asked suspiciously.

"I placed it under my pillow and slept on it," Noi replied. "The ghost commanded I throw the book out the window, but I kept it under my pillow. I watched the ghost shrink into nothingness and slip away into oblivion."

The pastor got up from his table and walked to his bookshelf. "You mean you didn't read the book?"

"No, Pastor Lek."

Pastor Lek took down the Bible he'd given her. "If you want true protection from the ghost, you have to do more than just hide it under your pillow."

"What should I do, pastor?"

"You need to read the book." He handed her the Bible.

Noi took the book home and, over time, read it from cover to cover. She came to understand the love of Jesus and that He was stronger than all the ghosts in the whole wide world. The night she began to read the Bible, the ghost didn't visit her. And from that day to this, Noi has never been bothered by ghosts ever again.

Chapter 6

Facing the Fangs

Mr. Lee's work unit in a hard-labor camp near the Tibetan mountains had the difficult task of breaking the ice to clear irrigation ditches so the water could flow to wheat fields for the benefit of the camp cadres. Hacking away at ice with pick and shovel in the cold late spring seemed harder when Mr. Lee knew he'd never eat even a mouthful of the wheat.

After he'd broken the ice into blocks and lifted them onto the bank, he had to be careful not to allow the icy water to seep into his boots where it could freeze. He recalled one prisoner who'd allowed his hands to get frostbitten. When the team returned to the burrow, he'd poured hot water over his hands, and his fingers fell off. No one in the camp could ever forget his screams.

Each prisoner had to clear one thousand feet of clogged canal every day. Anyone who didn't achieve his quota would be punished. Then they needed to load a wooden cart with the blocks of ice and haul them to the cooks.

"Load up!" the cart driver ordered at the end of the day. A guard hitched the horses to the cart, and the prisoners sat at the back, trying to avoid contact with the ice. The lash from the driver's whip startled the horses and they lurched forward.

The bumpy jostling ride to the prison compound was painful for Mr. Lee. He needed to stretch his legs.

"Whey! Whey!" Mr. Lee called repeatedly until he caught the driver's attention.

"What do you want?" the driver asked as he pulled the reins to slow the horses.

"The road's so rough it makes me sore." Mr. Lee flashed his charming smile.

35

"Request permission to walk back to camp."

The driver stopped and said, "You can walk back. I doubt you'll try to escape. But hurry. If you get lost and try to sleep out here, you'll never survive the cold. It's dangerous in these hills after dark, for tigers and bands of wild dogs are prowling in this area."

"Thank you. I'm not afraid. My Friend, Jesus, will protect me."

The driver didn't respect Mr. Lee's beliefs, but liked his work habits and trusted him. The guards and team leaders who'd observed Mr. Lee long enough became fond of him. Mr. Lee felt grateful to the driver as they exchanged farewell glances. "Be careful," the driver warned as the cart rolled on down the road. Mr. Lee watched it rattle and bounce until it disappeared around a bend. All alone, Mr. Lee felt the peaceful stillness of the greening fields flanked by the majestic Tibetan mountains. He loved a brisk walk and reveled in the natural beauty, enjoying this rare opportunity to appreciate the handiwork of the real God. Relaxed, he felt he had the whole world to himself.

After walking several miles, he noticed a rapid movement ahead. A band of wild dogs, having caught his scent, charged up the road toward him, with fierce eyes, rumbling growls, and barred teeth. He remembered rumors of hungry wild dogs near the compound being man-eaters, and he didn't wish to be lunch for these beasts.

On and on they came, salivating and growling in anticipation. Mr. Lee imagined them leaping through the air, knocking him down, tearing him into shreds, and gnawing on his bones. Trembling, he couldn't move, fearing his approaching death.

With no place to hide and no way to outrun the angry animals, he fell to his knees before the wild dogs, spread his arms wide in the form of a crucifix, closed his eyes, and prayed, "My Friend, Jesus, save my life from these dangerous dogs! Take away their appetite. You closed the mouths of hungry lions, preventing them from injuring Your servant Daniel. Because You protected Daniel in a den of lions, I know You can also shut the mouths of these wild dogs for me! Thank You, Jesus, my Friend, for helping me. Amen."

Mr. Lee heard a gentle whimper and opened his eyes. The wild dogs surrounded him with their tails tucked between their legs, transformed from ferocious to friendly. When he stood up, the dogs wagged their tails, inviting him to stroke behind their ears.

Facing the Fangs

A broad smile crossed Mr. Lee's face as they stretched out their forepaws and yawned in a little welcome dance. They seemed even to recognize him, or he suspected, they saw in him Someone Else. Squatting, he reached out his hand, and the wild dogs spilled over each other in their attempts to lick his palm. Their tongues felt wet and rough.

Suddenly, the dogs turned and ran up a hill. Mr. Lee resumed his walk, praising his Friend, Jesus!

Chapter 7

Arrested in Damascus!

Asher lived with his parents in Damascus, the Syrian city where God had once sent a blinded Paul to see Christ better. Today Damascus is an Islamic city, but Asher was raised a Christian. One day at family worship, his mother read a Bible verse, "The eye of the Lord runs to and fro watching whom He loves."

"What does that mean?" Father asked Mother.

"If someone has an eye on you," Mother answered, "you're special to that person, so this verse means we're precious to God, and He'll protect us."

Asher never forgot that promise. Its words rang in his head. If he was one of God's treasures, and other people were special to God as well and God would take care of His treasures, Asher wanted to do something for Him to help Muslims learn about their value to God. But what could he do? He was so young.

Then an idea came. After thinking about it a while, he told his parents he wanted to tell Muslims about Jesus. Father said, "Muslims know about Jesus. He's one of their six prophets."

"I know," Asher said, "but I want Muslims to know that when they do something wrong, Jesus will forgive them."

Father looked alarmed, "Son, it's too dangerous! Christians aren't allowed to share their beliefs with Muslims."

"Muslims don't know Jesus as their Savior." Asher looked up at his parents with eager eyes. "If they knew Jesus could save them, they wouldn't need to feel bad about their mistakes if they told Jesus they're sorry."

"I'm glad you want to do that, Asher," Mother said, "but if we let you talk to Muslims about Jesus, we'll always be afraid for you."

"But," a broad smile spread across Asher's face, "you taught me that the eye of the Lord runs to and fro. God will protect me." Father and Mother looked at each other. With Asher claiming a Bible promise, how could they not agree to his plan?

So Asher bought a bag with two sections and a secret pocket in the middle. He placed a variety of health books in both sections. Then he unzipped the secret pocket and carefully hid a few books telling about simple steps to Jesus. Christians in Damascus weren't allowed to sell their religious books to Muslims, but selling health books was permitted. Asher knew that health books often sparked a Muslim's interest in other Christian books. But—and this was what his parents feared—if the wrong person learned that Asher was showing Christian books to Muslims, the government might throw him in jail, or even sentence him to be hanged.

Asher knew this, too, but he believed that the eye of the Lord would protect him; so, with bag in hand, he visited Muslims one after another in their homes. In Damascus, people welcome strangers into their homes. They offer them food and tea and Turkish coffee. When they see an empty dish, or an empty cup, they fill it again and again. When they think they have provided enough food and beverage, they ask, "Now, what can we do for you?"

This was exactly what they did when Asher went visiting. They gave him food and beverages and after awhile asked, "What can we do for you?" When they said that, it was his chance.

When he first entered a home, Asher didn't give his name. He knew his name would betray him as Christian. In Muslim countries Muslims have Islamic names and Christians have Christian names. Common Muslim names are Mohammed, Mehmet, Ali, and Saddam. If Muslims knew he was Christian, they wouldn't listen to his message. So, when the people asked what they could do for him, Asher—without saying his name—opened his bag, pulled out a health book, and showed it to them. Often the book sold. Then, as he was leaving, Asher told them his name. "Oh, you're Christian," the people exclaimed and some of them asked, "Do you have any Christian books we can read?"

When they asked for Christian books, Asher, at the risk of his life, unzipped his secret pocket and pulled out a guide to Jesus. His hosts usually snatched up the book, reading it eagerly. When they learned that Jesus could save them from evil, many of them bought the book.

Each time Asher took out a Christian book for a Muslim to read, he knew their request might be a trick. Any Muslim could report him to the government. But day after day, he showed Muslims his books and nothing went awry.

One day Asher visited a man who lived alone in an unusually large house. The man served him food and drink like the other people and then asked what he could do for him. When he pulled out a health book, the man examined it and bought it. Then he asked, "What's your name?"

"Asher."

"Asher? Then you must be Christian. Do you have any Christian books I could read?" Asher dug into his secret pocket, pulled out a book, and gave it to him. He looked at it and asked the price. Asher told him.

"You know, this is against the law," the man warned.

"But Muslims need to know that they can be saved through Jesus Christ," Asher answered boldly.

Suddenly, the man's attitude changed. "I'm a member of the secret police," he announced. "You have broken the law, and I'm notifying the government." Quickly, the man locked the doors and bolted the windows; then he phoned the police to come to his house immediately.

"Stay there, boy! Don't try to escape!" he commanded Asher. "The house is locked. Only I can let you out—and I won't do that until the police arrive!"

The man stepped outside, locking the door behind him, and stood guard, waiting for the police. Inside the darkened house, Asher feared what might happen next. When he heard the sirens, he shivered. The police unlocked the door and hastily handcuffed him.

But as soon as he was handcuffed, Asher's fears vanished and he felt calm. He remembered, "The eye of the Lord runs to and fro." He knew God was watching him and would take care of him.

Asher kept his head high as the police pushed him outside and shoved him into the back seat of their squad car and drove away with siren blaring. Fully trusting God, Asher leaned back in his seat and enjoyed the ride.

The police pointed out a gallows in the city where a couple of Syrian bodies swung gently in the breeze. "That's what'll happen to you, boy!" the police laughed. "When we get you to court, the judge'll sentence you to be hanged like those low-life Israeli spies!" Asher said nothing.

The police escorted Asher into a courtroom where they accused him of selling Christian books to Muslims. "According to the law, he should be hanged!"

The judge looked down at Asher, then looked again. "How old are you?" he asked.

"Twelve."

"That's the problem," the judge said. "You're too young to be hanged. The court can't sentence you until you're eighteen." The police hollered that Asher should be killed. "He's the mother of all proselytizers! Kill him!"

"Order! Order!" demanded the judge. "The court rules that the defendant is to be released. But I warn you, boy," he said to Asher, "if you're ever caught again, we'll devise a way to kill you." Looking disappointed, the police removed the handcuffs and drove Asher home.

For three days, Asher felt too scared to leave his house. Then he remembered the verse about "the eye of the Lord." God would protect him. Soon he was out in another neighborhood, carrying his bag of health books—with hidden books guiding Muslims to Christ. God's eye did watch over him and he had no further trouble.

Years later, Asher—who wishes to remain anonymous—immigrated to the United States and studied to become a doctor. He is grateful to be able to teach about God through health. Today, when he considers how God has protected him and has led his life from his boyhood in Damascus to his adulthood as a doctor in the United States, Asher is certain that the eye of the Lord watches him and all His other treasured people.

Chapter 8

The Christmas Baby That Waited

The pastor's feet pounded against the dusty, parched path that ran between the thatched bamboo huts of his fellow Khmer refugees in the Nong Samet refugee camp between Thailand and Kampuchea (now Cambodia) in Southeast Asia. The whistling swoosh of Vietnamese rockets flying toward the camp interrupted his concentration. Would their enemy, the Vietnamese, invade the camp today, on Christmas—the day of peace and goodwill to all men?

A shell screamed as it arched toward the camp. The pastor willed himself to ignore the fact that more artillery fire than usual was targeting his camp. He had work to do. He must concentrate on choosing garments suitable for his performers' costumes. He hoped this year his church's Christmas play would persuade more refugees to believe in Jesus Christ as their Savior.

A rocket exploding nearby jolted his thoughts back to the Vietnamese. *Are they moving their equipment closer to launch an invasion?* Uncontrollable emotions welled up.

Why do the Vietnamese have control of my beloved country? he wondered. *Why won't they go back to Hanoi, where they belong? Are Khmers, like God's people Israel in the Bible, being made to suffer at the hands of their ancient bitter foes, the Vietnamese? Can't God find a better way to bring us closer to Him than by making us suffer war and persecution? Why would God let Hanoi invade defenseless refugees on, of all days, Christmas Day?*

An invasion didn't worry him so much for his own sake; he had already lost

The Christmas Baby That Waited

almost everything when he escaped from his home in Kampuchea. He'd fled once; he knew he'd escape again.

He worried more for his wife. Pregnant, she had gone into intense labor on Christmas Eve. He was excited about becoming a father—and, no less, a father of a Christmas child. But if the baby came today—if it did—and the Vietnamese did stage an invasion, would his wife be able to escape safely to Khao-I-Dang camp, across Thailand's border?

His steps quickened on the dirt road toward the clinic. *Will our baby be born today?*

Inside the clinic, the French doctor from Doctors Without Borders forced a smile.

"How is she, Doctor?"

"Your wife *ees* in *heave* labor," he replied with a soft, but prominent French accent. "You'll be a father any time now."

"What about the Vietnamese attack?"

"In my experience as a doctor, I have learned one thing for sure."

"What's that, Doctor?" the pastor asked.

The doctor's face spread into a wise smile. "Babies come when they are ready to come. Your baby won't wait."

"And if there's an invasion?"

"I tell you, the baby does not know anything about an invasion, so it will still come just the same." The doctor reflected, then said, "If there is an evacuation, your wife will be too weak to walk to Khao-I-Dang. You'll have to leave her behind. Maybe the Vietnamese won't destroy the hospital, *oui*?" The doctor tried to end on an upbeat note, but he knew his words hadn't been comforting. "I'm sorry, Pastor," he said. "Let's hope there's no evacuation."

"Could she make it to Khao-I-Dang if the baby didn't come?"

"Her labor's intense, Pastor. That baby's due very soon. But if her labor were to stop, *oui,* she could make it if you protected her belly from being crushed in the crowd."

"I'll pray." The pastor hurried out of the clinic. "Thank you, Doctor," he called over his shoulder.

He didn't bother going to his church. The Christmas play was probably finished, or more likely, canceled. Instead, he found himself heading toward his hut. He must gather his few belongings together, for if he was to live, he must flee.

Miracles in Unexpected Places

As he packed a few essentials, he pleaded with God: "Lord, why do You let the enemy harass us today on Your birthday? If it's Your will, persuade the Vietnamese to stop attacking. But if they must invade us, please, if it is Your will, perform a miracle for us today. I know that all things are possible for You, Lord." When he realized he was praying aloud, his voice cracked, and his vision blurred from tears.

He stopped packing and knelt on his bamboo bed. "My wife will have a child soon. But if she delivers today, she and her baby will die at the hand of the Vietnamese invaders. That baby makes a great Christmas present, Lord, but why take it away the same day? I've lost almost everything. Please, don't take away my wife and child! Lord, let the baby wait to be born until its mother is safe. This I pray in the name of Your Son whose birth we celebrate today. Thank You. Amen."

He stood on the packed-dirt floor, dried his eyes, and threw together his last few things: Just a pot, a pan, a Khmer-English dictionary, and a Bible. Time was running out. The Vietnamese artillery fire was heavy. He could hear their tanks rolling.

On his way back to the clinic the pastor continued to pray silently. *Will the Lord grant my prayer? Can my wife escape? Must I flee alone?*

Crowds from the camp were already trekking out toward Khao-I-Dang when the pastor pressed his way into the clinic. The doctor was still there, but the clinic showed signs that he, too, planned to evacuate. He'd already packed most of the equipment, and the clinic stood almost empty.

The doctor saw the pastor and came over to him. "I can't believe what's happened. Your wife's labor stopped half an hour ago. I have never before seen something like that. I don't know how to explain it."

The pastor knew. Precisely half an hour earlier he'd knelt on his bamboo bed pleading with God for a miracle!

He saw his wife, large with child, smiling at him. "Can she make the trip, Doctor?"

"I think she'll be all right." The doctor caught the pastor's joy, and soon two smiles radiated.

A rocket explosion reminded them they'd better evacuate to Khao-I-Dang.

Their escape came none too soon. Almost immediately afterward, Vietnamese tanks rolled in. Driving back and forth over the camp, they flattened every building, including the clinic. After the pastor and his wife crossed the border into Thailand safely, they looked back in time to watch their camp go up in flames. Sadly, tanks, bullets, and flames don't distinguish holidays.

So December 25, 1984, became a Christmas sixty-two thousand Khmer refugees would never forget. That day they lost their homes, but all escaped safely into Thailand's Khao-I-Dang refugee camp.

The Christmas baby was born in Bang Phu. The pastor and his wife thought no family was ever more happy to have a child than they. Together they prayed: "Lord, thank You for the belated Christmas baby. Making it come late was the best Christmas present You could give us. We thank You that we escaped safely, and that everyone else in Nong Samet escaped death. Sometimes, Lord, we wish we didn't have to go through trials like these, but, with Your protection, Christmas this year was almost as wonderful as the one when You were born. Thank You for building our faith and for showing Your greatness through the miracle of the Christmas baby that waited."

The author was in Khao-I-Dang on the Christmas that the Vietnamese attacked Nong Samet. He has personally met the pastor in this story.

Chapter 9

Mr. Brown and the Model T

"How are you feeling, dearie?" old Mr. Brown asked his wife tenderly. Hoping to better hear her reply, he leaned over in the chair where he'd been sitting by her bed.

"I'm all right, Mr. Brown, considering." Mrs. Brown tried to smile but was able to lift only one corner of her mouth.

"Considering what, my dear?" Mr. Brown asked.

"That the pain could be worse," his wife replied.

"Is your pain worse?" Mr. Brown asked. "Do you think we should go see the doctor?"

"Oh, can we go to the doctor?" old Mr. Brown's wife asked. "It's such a long journey, and I'm very weak. Besides, are you sure the doctor would see me? We haven't paid him for the last visit yet."

Mr. Brown was at a loss for words. His wife had a point. The times had become hard for the family after his wife had gotten sick. Mr. Brown had opted to spend every moment he could at her bedside, trying to make sure she was as comfortable as possible. He took her to the doctor whenever she absolutely needed to see one, but doctors charged fees for their visits, and Mr. Brown wasn't making much money while he was taking care of the woman he loved.

And then there was the problem with the Model T. It was unpredictable about starting, and the engine died at unexpected times. Mr. Brown would jump out of the car and scratch his head as he peered into or under the engine

Mr. Brown and the Model T

trying to discover what he might do to make it work again. Whenever that happened, old Mr. Brown would hear people trotting by with their horse and buggies advising, "Get a horse!" then laugh. Oh, how Mr. Brown hated that laugh.

But, Mr. Brown reminded himself, there was nothing to be done about their taunts. He felt certain that Ford's new horseless contraptions would soon be everywhere and that the horse-drawn carriage would someday become a relic.

Then there was the question of money for the doctor. He didn't want to think how much was already on his tab. Turning to his wife he said, "If you're feeling worse, I'll get the old Model T out and take you to the doctor." Mr. Brown put his hand on her forehead, then on his. "You're pretty warm. Say nothing about the doctor's bill. I think we better see him. Here, let me help you out of bed and into the old Model T." Lovingly, he helped ease his wife out of bed and, placing his arm around her, guided her through the house and out into the yard, where he opened the passenger door and set her in the seat. "Are you comfortable, dear?" he asked.

When she nodded, Mr. Brown said, "Now all we have to do is get the engine running and we'll be off." In those days starting a car was not as easy as putting a key into the ignition and turning it. After setting the shift into drive, Mr. Brown had to grab the crank, go to the front of the car, fit it in the slot, and turn the heavy crank one revolution. This he did, jumping in the process.

"*Putt,*" said the engine.

Mr. Brown tried again, jumping a bit higher as he spun the crank.

"*Putt,*" spat the Model T.

Overcoming his frustration, he energetically jumped again as the crank revolved in the keyhole.

"*Putt, putt,*" replied the car.

Encouraged, Mr. Brown cranked again.

"*Putt, putt, putt!*"

"You almost got it, Mr. Brown, dear," said his wife.

Enthusiastically Mr. Brown spun the crank, making an involuntary jump in the process.

"*Putt, putt, putt, varoooooooooooom, chug, chug, chug!*" The Model T burst into life and began rolling toward Mr. Brown, who deftly leaped out of the vehicle's way.

"Hold, on, dearie," Mr. Brown shouted to his wife. "I gotta catch up with

47

this ol' car and jump into the driver's seat. If it gets too far ahead of me, you might need to stomp on the brake." It took a little running alongside the Ford, but soon he had his hand on the black roof then hastily dove feet-first into the seat behind the steering wheel. After emitting a relieved sigh and dropping the crank on the floor beside his wife, Mr. Brown began steering happily.

The car rattled and popped down the dirt road, jostling the worried couple along its merry way toward the doctor's home.

Suddenly, in the middle of nowhere, the car abruptly stopped.

"What happened?" Mrs. Brown asked.

"I don't know, dearie," Mr. Brown answered as he reached for the crank and hopped out of the car. Going around to the front, he fitted the crank into the slot and spun it with an involuntary jump for emphasis.

Nothing happened.

He did it again.

Nothing.

After spinning it the third time with no results, Mr. Brown lifted the hood and looked inside. Just then, seemingly from nowhere, a horse and buggy drove by. The man on the buggy seat noticed Mr. Brown and asked sarcastically, "What's wrong? Need a horse?"

"I'll be fine," Mr. Brown said under his breath as the buggy passed. Lifting his head from the engine area, he bumped it on the hood. "Ow!" He rubbed his forehead until if felt better.

As the buggy driver continued down the road, he looked over his shoulder and shouted, "Get a horse!" His cackling laughter seemed to echo across the valley.

"Honey," said Mrs. Brown, "don't forget what they say sometimes. If the engine won't start, look underneath; the engine might've dropped out."

Mr. Brown smiled to himself. He was looking at the engine, and it hadn't dropped out. However, his wife did have a point. Perhaps a part of the engine had come loose and fallen to the ground. "It won't hurt to look," he called to his wife. Getting down on his hands and knees, Mr. Brown ducked his head and peered under the Model T.

"See anything?" his wife asked.

"Ah, no—wait!"

"You see something?"

Mr. Brown and the Model T

"I see something that might be a screw." He reached for it. That's strange. It's green. Mr. Brown brought it closer and saw that it was covered in oil, but that it was no screw. It was a roll of green paper. As he started to unroll it, he shouted, "Money. I found a roll of money!"

It definitely was a wad of dollar bills. Judging from how dirty and grimy they appeared, it seemed they might have been there for quite some time. Considering that the Model T unceremoniously broke down right on top of the roll of cash added to the mystery.

After Mr. Brown climbed back into the car, he counted out the money. "There is more than enough money here to pay the doctor for all his visits and for this one."

"What are we going to do with the money, dear?" Mr. Brown's wife asked.

"I suppose, dearie," Mr. Brown replied, "that we can ask around town to see if anyone's missing any." He slipped the greasy roll into his shirt pocket. "Once in town, I'm sure God will help us know what to do about it."

"We need to get to town first," his wife calmly stated the obvious.

Mr. Brown nodded, "We need to crank up that stubborn Model T engine so it's running again."

To Mr. Brown's eyes, his wife seemed to have a little more color in her face already. "I feel that God is with us, Mr. Brown. Why don't we pray," she said softly, "and ask God to help the Model T to start?" This is exactly what they did.

After they finished praying, Mr. Brown snatched the crank, climbed down from the car, and headed for the front. He slid the crank into the slot and then turned it, making another of his involuntary jumps.

"Putt, putt, varoooooooooom, chugachugachug!" The Model T roared into life and jerked forward, gathering speed. Again Mr. Brown sidestepped the approaching car and jogged beside it until he could again jump into the driver's seat and steer the vehicle down the road.

With considerably lighter hearts, the old couple neared the doctor's home, knowing it would be a day that they'd never forget—the day that the Model T broke down and God answered their prayer.

Chapter 10

The Large Bar of Soap

Robert Huang wanted a Bible to read. He couldn't ask for one because he wasn't allowed to have one. Robert was languishing in a Shanghai prison. He sat on the floor of his cell waiting to be sentenced. He'd been arrested because he was an active pastor of the underground church in Shanghai after the Chinese government had locked the doors of all but the government church.

After four years of waiting to be sentenced, Robert heard the prison authorities announce that prisoners would be allowed to write one letter to their families. "But you must use no more than one hundred Chinese characters."

Robert reminded himself, "One hundred Chinese characters is so little. It's not even a hundred words because some words in Chinese take more than one character. How can you summarize four years for your family in less than a hundred words?" Then he remembered his wish for a Bible.

Feeling depressed and lacking the boldness to put God to a direct test, he began to pray. "Lord, help me communicate to my family that I need a Bible. Help me think of some way to ask for one without the guards knowing what I'm asking for."

"Pttkkt!" The loudspeaker in the prison crackled and someone at the microphone cleared a throat, "Ahem, prisoner 115, prepare for visitation. Prisoner 115, prepare for visitation."

All of the prisoners had numbers. None of them were called by their names. Robert had his own number, Criminal 426. It was a means of dehumanizing the prisoners by depriving them of their identities. Robert hated having a number for a name—except when he could use the number to witness to a fellow inmate. Clearing his head, Robert tried to pray again. "Lord, help me think of a covert way to ask for a Bible."

"*Pttkt!*" The loud speaker shrieked, interrupting Robert's prayer. "Prisoner 115—it's visitation time."

Placing his hands over his ears to drown out the speaker, Robert prayed, "How do I surreptitiously ask for a Bible?"

"*Pttkt!* It's visitation time for prisoner 115!"

Robert grew impatient. "Lord, I'm trying to pray to You, but I keep getting interrupted by the loud speaker. How can I hear Your still, small voice with all this racket?"

"*Pttkkkt!* Prisoner 115, you have five minutes for visitation."

"Lord, are You hearing me?" Robert pleaded in exasperation. "I can't hear You. Please make it quiet. I can't concentrate." Then an idea came to his head. *The number 115 reminds me of something. What could it be?* He thought hard, knowing the number must be significant. Suddenly, his eyes lit up and he smiled. Yeah, that's it. In the Chinese hymnal, hymn number 115 is "Give me the Bible." Instantly, while overcome with shame that he hadn't trusted God more, Robert folded his hands and prayed. "I'm sorry, Lord. You were trying to answer my prayer, but I was too busy being frustrated with the announcer on the loudspeaker to realize it. I wanted a subtle way to communicate—and You delivered it in a loud, yet clandestine way. Thank You for being there for me."

Robert pounded on the cell wall, and soon a guard answered. "What do you want, Criminal 426?"

"I need paper and pen to write a letter to my family, sir."

The guard disappeared down the hallway and soon returned with paper and a pen in his hand. "Remember," the guard reminded, "you can only write one hundred Chinese characters. You can't say anything bad about the food, and you should let people know you're being treated well."

"As to the food and my treatment by the guards, you needn't worry. On those accounts, I have nothing to complain about." Robert replied. "I just want to talk with my family." *Something I haven't been able to do for four years,* he thought to himself, but dared not say, fearful it would put the guard in a bad mood. "If you let me write to them, I will have absolutely nothing to complain about."

"I see," the guard replied as he handed the paper and pen to Robert. "When you're done, Criminal 426, knock. I'll pick up your letter and read it."

"I understand, sir." Robert sighed. That his private words to his family needed to be read by a guard rankled him. But there was nothing he could do about it, so, Robert reasoned, it wouldn't do any good to complain about that either. When it came to expressing complaints, as far as he was concerned, the guard would have nothing to worry about.

"If the letter's all right," the guard continued, "we'll make sure your family gets it."

"Thank you, sir," Robert said.

After the guard left, Robert picked up the pen and tried to think what to say. Lacking the faith to let God perform an outright miracle on his behalf if He so wished, Robert decided to help God out a little by writing his request in code. Having made up his mind, he began writing fast and furiously: "I want a 115-page notebook. If it's not 115 pages I don't want it. Kindly make sure the notebook has 115 pages or don't bring it. Oh, and I'd also like a bar of soap, Brand 39." Setting his pen down, Robert hastily read over his letter, counting carefully to make sure that he had not exceeded the one-hundred-character limit. Thinking it satisfactory, he then banged on the wall and waited for the guard to reappear.

Soon the guard came and Robert handed him the letter. Mumbling to himself, the guard read it aloud haltingly. Robert held his breath, fearful that the guard might remember that there were no 115-page notebooks in China and that there is no Brand 39 soap; it's actually Brand 36. Robert had added the request for the soap to refer to the number of books found in the Old Testament.

Looking up from the letter the guard said, "You made no complaints. That's nice." Folding it up, he placed it in his shirt pocked. "I'll deliver it to her personally!" With that, the guard marched away.

Robert was initially elated that his letter had been accepted. The guard had not cracked the code Robert had used. He didn't understand that the number 115 referred to a song title requesting a Bible or that the Brand 39 soap referred to the number of books in the Old Testament. Then Robert began to have doubts. If the guard had not understood the code, what if his family couldn't understand what he wanted? Had he been too subtle? But worrying would make little difference now. All he could do was wait until his number was called

The Large Bar of Soap

for his five-minute visitation with his family and hope. Hope was better than worry. He determined to keep hoping and set worry aside.

Time seemed to pass slowly as he sat waiting for the floor in his cell to rot. It was what one of the guards had said, "Which do you think will rot first—you or the floor of your cell? Talk to us, tell us your crimes, and the government will be merciful." They had been "merciful" enough to place him under arrest without a charge and interrogate him periodically to try to make him confess.

Robert was an ABC, an American-born Chinese, living in Shanghai after the war between the Communists and the Nationalists. After Nationalist President Chiang Kai-shek had been defeated by Communist Chairman Mao Zedong, he had crossed the Taiwan Strait and set up a new capital in Taipei. A Bamboo Curtain fell between Mainland China and Taiwan, both governments claiming to be the real China. The American Embassy fled Communist China and had reopened in Taipei. When Robert's American passport expired, he couldn't renew it because he wasn't allowed to go to Taipei.

After the Communist takeover of Shanghai, the government initially cracked down on businesses, arresting and imprisoning businessmen. Once the government had shut down or taken over all the businesses in the city, it began to shut down and control religion.

Robert was under suspicion by the government for two crimes.* First, he had been born in America, and second, he was an active pastor after the government had officially closed all church doors except the government-run Three-Self Church. His American-born status made the government suspicious of his loyalty to China, so on that point alone he was watched and sometimes questioned, but the government was far more worried because they suspected that he was going to people's homes and conducting clandestine church services. While they were obviously suspicious, it was evident to Robert that they had no proof—despite all the guards' professions of knowing all his crimes.

How merciful would they be if he told them what they wanted to hear? Visitation with his family had been denied for four years; then the policy had suddenly changed, and all the inmates were granted, whenever their names were called over the loudspeaker, five-minute visitations with their families.

---

* In the tradition of Daniel, this author maintains that civil disobedience is biblical, and he makes a distinction between a sin and a crime. He reasons that a crime is not always a sin, whereas most sins are crimes. When a law goes against the moral code of God, it is a sin to obey.

Miracles in Unexpected Places

What could you tell your family in just five minutes after being unable to communicate with them for four years? Robert's mind began to spin just thinking about it.

Days went by, then he heard it. He actually heard it, despite his disbelieving ears. *"Pttkkt!"* the loudspeaker notoriously squawked. "Criminal 426, prepare for visitation. Criminal 426, prepare for visitation. Your family is here to see you."

Eagerly, Robert began preparations. Finding his best clothes, he changed into them. Taking out his comb, he wrestled with his unruly hair until it looked somewhat kempt. Then he paced the room, waiting for the guard to escort him to the visitation room. The loudspeaker squawked, *"Pttkt!* Criminal 426, it's time for your visitation."

He heard the rattling of the key as the guard unlocked the door to his cell and opened it. After stepping into Robert's cell, the guard announced, "Criminal 426, follow me."

Robert followed the guard down the hall to the visitation room. As the guard frisked Robert, he instructed, "Remember, you have only *five minutes*! You cannot say anything bad about the food or anything bad about your treatment in prison. We take good care of you! No physical contact. If you break any of these rules, your visit will be instantly terminated, and you will be responsible for the consequences!"

Robert's face may have inadvertently revealed his disappointment at the thought of not being able to even shake his mother's hand. The guard looked him in the eye and shouted, "Do you understand?"

Robert nodded.

"Any questions?"

Robert shook his head.

"You may enter at my word, and the clock will start ticking!"

Robert stepped toward the door and waited.

"Go now!" The guard commanded, "Remember no touching! You have five minutes. Make good use of your time."

Robert raced into the room filled with cubicles. Guards eavesdropped as they moved from one cubicle to the next. Then he saw his mother motion for him to come. Sitting beside her was his eldest sister. Quickly he sat across from them. It felt wonderful to see them. Both of them wore huge smiles. What could he say in five minutes? Where to begin? There were two things he wanted to know.

The first question was whether his girlfriend still loved him. He wanted to tell her that if she felt her biological clock was ticking and that if she found a better man, she should take him. But something prevented Robert from saying those words.

Before he could ask, his sister answered his first question, saying. "Mary told us to tell you that if you still want her, she will wait for you."

Relief flooded through him. "I want her!" he replied. "I'm glad she'll wait!"

Then he wanted to know if they had brought him a Bible.

Suddenly it seemed, before he could say another word, the guards were shouting, "Your five minutes are up. Go back to your cell."

Oh, the tyranny of time, Robert thought. Guards approached to escort him out on his side while other guards began escorting his mother and sister out on their side. Anxiety filled Robert as he wondered when he might see them again. There was so much to say that hadn't been said.

And what about the Bible?

Robert's sister was also fearful of being arrested, or even killed, if she mentioned the Bible. While she was being escorted toward the exit, a clever idea crossed her mind. She managed to call over her shoulder, "I sent you a large bar of soap. You might want to break it in half because it's so big." Then, still looking anxious, she disappeared behind the closing doors.

The guard escorted him back to his room. *So they've sent me a large bar of soap,* Robert mused. He'd asked for soap, but it was code. *Did they take my request literally? If so, how will I get a Bible now?* The guard arrived at Robert's cell and unlocked it, ushered him in, and locked it behind him. There was nothing for Robert to do but sit and wait for the gifts his family had left him to be delivered after they were inspected.

In what seemed like an eternity, a guard delivered a package. Robert, realizing that he couldn't be too careful, took some of his soiled clothes with him and sat down facing a wall so that his back was to his fellow inmate and any guard who might pass by. He reasoned that if there were a Bible inside, he didn't want anyone to know. Slowly and carefully, he opened the package. Inside he found that, sure enough, it contained an extremely large bar of soap. He lifted it to see if they had hidden a Bible underneath, but he was disappointed. All that was in the package was, as his sister had said, a large bar of soap—no Bible or anything else. Apparently he had been too opaque in his letter.

Then he remembered that his sister had said, "Break the bar of soap in half because it's so large." Leaning over the bag so as to make it less visible to anyone around him, Robert broke the bar. Inside, to his joy, he found an English pocket Bible. Instantly, he stuffed it into the safest place he could think of—his underwear. Then, as he began to wash some of his laundry by hand, he considered what to do with his new treasure.

After Robert finished washing, he announced to his cellmates, "I want to move my bed to the other side of the cell."

"You mean over near the bars at the hall, which is always lighted?"

"Precisely," Robert replied. "That means you can sleep in the darker section of the cell and nearer to the toilet. Would you consider that trade?"

"Sounds good to me," one of his fellow inmates replied. "It's not easy to sleep near the hall—what with the light and the footfall of the guard waking you up every time he walks by."

"Yeah," said the other fellow inmate. "It's fine with me. We'll help you." And that is exactly what they did.

That night Robert lay awake in his bed listening to the footfall of the guard as he made his rounds in the prison. When he heard that the footfall was at the other end of the prison, he cautiously pulled his precious pocket Bible out of his underwear and began to read. When the footsteps got louder, he buried the book safely under the covers and back into his underwear. Forgetting that he was already imprisoned and could no longer be arrested, or that God could do wonders if given the opportunity, Robert feigned sleep before the guard could look into his room. Robert returned to his reading when he heard the guard pacing at the other end of the prison.

Eventually, he dozed off around sunup only to be awakened by shouting and commotion. All the prisoners were peering out the bars of their cells into the hall to learn what the excitement was all about. Robert saw a hapless inmate being paraded down the hall. A guard was forcing the inmate's head down, trying to shame him. Another guard shouted repeatedly, "You can't fool the Chinese Liberation Army. If you do, we will find you out. If you try, you will be responsible for the consequences."

As the prisoner neared Robert's cell, Robert saw that the doomed inmate was wearing what resembled a pendant around his neck. Knowing that no one was allowed to wear jewelry in the prison, Robert strained his eyes to see what it really was. It was a string and what had looked like a pendant was only a sewing needle.

The guards yelled, "This criminal's family tried to hide a sewing needle in a bar of soap, but the Chinese Liberation Army discovered it. You can't fool the Chinese Liberation Army. If you try to, we will find you out. This criminal is living proof. Disobey prison rules and you'll have only yourself to blame for the punishment you deserve. Be forewarned." Robert and the other prisoners watched until the unfortunate prisoner was marched away to receive his fate.

Tired though he was, Robert sat back on his bed and marveled at the miracle God had performed for him. The Chinese Liberation Army had found a needle hidden in a bar of soap, Robert mused to himself, but they had missed his pocket Bible. Truly, his was a miracle Bible. Surely God wanted him to read His Word while behind bars. And despite Robert's lack of faith that God could perform wonders—and unlike Daniel's three friends standing before Nebuchadnezzar at the burning fiery furnace—he'd been unwilling to accept the consequences should God have chosen not to rescue him. God had indeed miraculously delivered a Bible to him. *Wow!* Robert thought to himself. *What miracles might God have performed had he exercised more faith?* Closing his eyes, Robert asked God to help his unbelief and thanked Him for showing that He cared for him and for his pocket English Bible.

Chapter 11

Daddy Discovers Time for His Bible

One thing Dakota could be certain about was that her father, Mr. R. B. Schwartz, loved her. He tried to do everything he could to make her happy. He bought her nice clothes, got her a pet parakeet, some pet monkeys, and an adorable little Yorkshire terrier named Bowser. When she went to the ice cream parlor, he knew her favorite flavor. He never missed taking her to the fair; there she could go on any ride she liked. On her birthday she could do anything she wanted. He took her on vacation trips to Hawaii and Mexico. And he promised that when she was old enough to drive, he'd buy her a brand-new Ford Mustang convertible.

Dakota's father owned Schwartz Oil Company, a full-service gas station with the lowest prices for miles around. She loved working for her dad.

As it was a full-service station, whenever customers drove up to the pump, they didn't need to get out to pump gas themselves. All they needed to do was roll down the window and Dakota would ask, "Fill 'er up? Premium or regular?"

Most of the customers chose regular because it cost less. If they didn't want to fill up the tank, they'd tell Dakota how much to put in, by saying something like, "Put in five gallons please."

With a warm smile, she'd follow their instructions, happily pumping the gas into their vehicle. While the gas was pouring in, Dakota would wash their windows. Then she'd return to the window and say, "Spring the hood." Going around to the front, she'd lift the hood, prop it up, and check the dipstick. If the oil was low, she'd pour in half a quart or more, then show the customer that all was well.

Dakota's cheerful way of serving customers ensured they'd return.

Having been raised a Sabbath keeper since his childhood and deciding to begin keeping Sabbath again, Dakota's father barricaded the entrance to his station one Friday evening, planning to remove the barricades Saturday night. His competitors laughed, saying that as Saturday was the busiest day, he'd soon close his doors permanently. They predicted they'd get all his Saturday business.

On that first weekend that Mr. Schwartz had closed his gas station, Dakota had wondered what would happen Saturday evening. After sundown, she, her mom, and her dad drove to the station. Dakota half expected to see only a dark street and an empty barricaded gas station. But as they neared the station, Dakota's eyes opened wide with surprise. There on the road was a line of cars leading to the entrance of her father's station. Evidently her father wouldn't be going out of business.

With his low prices and his full-service policy, his customers were willing to wait until sundown Saturday to buy their gas. The owners of the other companies scratched their heads and lowered their prices so they could compete. But none of them closed their businesses on Saturday.

Dakota was thankful and praised God that her father was now closing the station on Sabbaths.

God blessed R. B. Schwartz for keeping the Sabbath, and his business grew. On a hunch that the price of rubber would rise during the war, he bought a warehouse and filled it with automobile tires.

His hunch proved right, and he was expecting a tidy profit. Driving in his new Ford convertible with his wife and daughter one day, he saw black smoke billowing into the sky and pointed it out to his family.

"That smoke appears to be very close to your warehouse with all those tires," his wife said. "With smoke that dark, it could be burning rubber."

Dakota gasped.

"It's probably not," Dakota's father said hopefully, trying to encourage his family.

"Let's check it out," Dakota's mother urged. "I could sleep better if I knew all was well."

"All right." Father turned onto another road, heading toward the smoke.

"I wonder where the fire engines are," Dakota marveled. "Haven't they been alerted?"

"The smoke is dying down now," Mother observed. "Perhaps the fire is almost under control."

After turning the car down yet another road, Dakota's father hit the brakes in surprise. The family could scarcely believe what they saw. In the place where father's tire warehouse had stood was a pile of red-hot smoldering ashes. The investment in tires had literally gone up in smoke. The ride back home was somber.

Something happened shortly after the warehouse burned that disappointed Dakota. Her father sold Schwartz Oil Company and began an ice cream franchise, which he called Zesty Ice Cream Parlor. Actually, that wasn't what disappointed her. What disappointed Dakota was that her father stopped closing his business on Sabbath. He felt he no longer had time to attend church; however, he was still very supportive of his wife's and his daughter's religion.

Dakota wanted her father to join her and her mother Sabbath mornings when they went to church. One Sabbath morning she begged, "Daddy, I wish you'd go to church with us today."

"Oh, I'm sorry, dearie. I can't go to church with you now," her father replied. "I have to work to earn the money to provide for your Christian education, and your promised Mustang convertible, not to mention that fine fur coat you're wearing," he said, trying to find an excuse for breaking the Sabbath and for his waning faith in Jesus.

"Oh, Daddy," Dakota pleaded, "The fur coat is really nice, but I don't care about the fur coat or the convertible. All I want is for you to sit beside me in church."

"Thank you, darling, for inviting me." Mr. Schwartz smiled at his daughter. "I appreciate it, but don't forget, education in an Adventist school isn't cheap," her father explained. "If I don't earn the money, you can't attend classes."

Dakota opened her mouth to reply but bit her tongue instead. She knew it would do her no good to persist, so she decided to remember her father in her prayers.

"Run along," her father said. "You don't want to be late for church." He hugged Dakota and her mother goodbye, and they left as her father headed off to work.

Daddy Discovers Time for His Bible

As the weeks turned into months which became years, her father still kept his business open every Sabbath. Dakota began praying that God would do something to awaken her father spiritually. After seeing no immediate results to her prayer, she decided to write out her prayer and present it to him.

And that's exactly what she did. She mailed her prayer to her father. When he received it, this is what he read: "Daddy, I'm praying that you'll get rebaptized and start attending church again with us. I told the Lord to take my life if it would bring you back to God."

After reading Dakota's letter, her father stepped outside and took a long walk as he thought things through.

Later that afternoon Dakota called from her boarding school. Her mother picked up the phone. "Did Daddy get my letter?" Dakota asked.

"He did," her mother replied.

"What happened?"

"He went for a walk," her mother said. "When he returned, he shared your letter with me and said solemnly, 'I think Dakota really wants to see me in heaven.'"

"Do you think he'll start going to church again?" Dakota asked.

"We'll see," was all her mother could say.

Dakota's father still didn't change his habits.

God did hear Dakota's prayer, but He had other plans in how to answer it.

It was said of R. B. Schwartz that if you took away all his money, leaving him with just the clothes on his back, all you'd need to do was wait a few months, and he'd be back in business. He'd sell that last shirt on his back and start manufacturing more shirts from his profits. He seemed to have that golden touch that Midas could only envy.

And envy got him into trouble. The managers of the franchises Mr. Schwartz sold banded together and took him to court, accusing him of breaking the law. Dakota's father told his lawyer that he was innocent. He'd broken no laws. "I follow the letter of the law. I'll admit that California has had to rewrite some of its laws because of the way I interpreted them, but I've never broken a law."

"Why do you think you're being sued?" his lawyer asked.

"I take my earnings and plow them right back into the cash register, so to speak," he replied. "By reinvesting it all, I grow the business."

"How can you pay your bills?"

"The franchisees need to pay me a percentage of their profits," Mr. Schwartz explained with a smile. "That's where my salary is."

"Very clever," the lawyer nodded and grinned. "I see you've broken no law. We'll do the best we can for you."

"That's what I pay you for," Dakota's father said.

"This should be an open-and-shut case," the lawyer attested.

However, as the trial wore on, it bogged down. One day the judge took Mr. Schwartz aside and sighed, "I'm not quite sure how to rule in this case."

"What seems to be the problem?" Mr. Schwartz asked.

"The plaintiffs have paid me money to rule against you, but I can't find a good reason to comply," the judge looked troubled. "I need your help."

"What would you like me to do?"

"I've got a proposition for you." The judge shifted his feet.

"What's that?"

"If you'd offer me a higher price than the prosecution, I'd rule in your favor."

Mr. Schwartz's mouth dropped momentarily. "You want a bribe?"

"It would help me make a decision easier."

Dakota's father thought quickly. He knew where this could lead. If he gave the judge the money he wanted, the judge would require more from the plaintiffs. This judge could blackmail both sides indefinitely until one side ran out of money. It wasn't hard for Dakota's father to know what to do. Looking the judge in the eye, Mr. Schwartz spoke calmly. "Evidently, you don't understand me, do you?"

"Help me," the judge urged.

Mr. Schwartz smiled, "I'm accused of breaking the law in my business practices, but I've done no such thing. These men are jealous because I'm successful and they're not. If they were more frugal like me, they'd be making as much as I am."

"So it would seem," the judge affirmed. "But they've given me money to bend my ear."

Mr. Schwartz continued, "You want me to break the law by offering a bribe. If I did that, I'd break the law, and you'd have every reason to put me behind bars."

"But if you don't, I'll be forced to rule against you," the judge sighed again. "I really don't want to do that."

Daddy Discovers Time for His Bible

Dakota's father stroked his chin in thought. "It looks like I'll be sent to jail either way," he said. "If I'm to serve a prison sentence, I'd rather do my time knowing I'm innocent rather knowing I deserved to be there."

"That's commendable. I understand how you feel, Mr. Schwartz. I was hoping it wouldn't turn out this way. I really wanted to rule in your favor," the judge said. Avoiding eye contact, the judge continued, "Regretfully, now I'll have no choice. I think we can wrap up this case rather quickly."

Indeed, it ended in the next court session with R. B. Schwartz receiving time behind bars.

Soured by the legal system, Dakota's father didn't bother to submit an appeal. Thinking the next judge might be as corrupt as the first, it seemed that using a higher court would be just a waste of time and resources. Instead, he quietly showed up to serve his time.

Life was hard for the family with Dakota's father in prison. The ice cream business closed down, and Dakota's mom tried to make ends meet by helping farmers pick berries. Dakota and her mother lived without the finer things of life that Mr. Schwartz had once provided. Soon they learned to be content in whatever condition they were in.

Meanwhile, back in prison, R. B. Schwartz felt shamed, humiliated, disgraced, and betrayed. This was a chapter in his life he'd like to skip. Bored, with nothing to sell and no one who wanted to buy, he sat on his bed wondering what to do. He discovered he had the rare gift of free time. He'd always been busy earning money for his family, but those days were gone. How would they survive? Until his sentence was completed, doing business was impossible. Looking around in his cell, he picked up the prison Bible, opened it, and began reading.

As he turned the pages in the Bible, Mr. Schwartz's experience with an unfair trial enabled him to read the Gospels with new insight. He saw that Jesus' trial had also been unfair, that His judges also refused to mete out justice, and that one of his friends betrayed Him. As he turned the pages of the age-old story, he marveled at the way Jesus treated those who mistreated Him. Mr. Schwartz vowed to follow Jesus' example. He decided that, after he got out of jail, he'd invite those who'd placed him there over to his house for lunch. He'd treat them as if nothing had ever happened.

The more he read his Bible, the more he learned. Soon he was studying the

Book carefully. The Holy Spirit worked on his heart, and he remembered his daughter's wish.

He recalled his childhood back in Oklahoma when his family kept the Sabbath. And the days before the warehouse burned when he'd closed Schwartz Oil Company on Friday and reopened after sundown Saturday. The Lord had blessed him. *What happened to my faith after the tires burned?* He asked himself. Because of his lack of faith, he'd lost his business, his lifestyle, and his reputation. *Have I lost my family also?* He wondered if his wife would still want him after his sentence was completed.

Then, to his surprise, one day the guards announced that he had a visitor. It was his wife. "I miss you," she said. "I know you're innocent and that the judge was unjust."

Mr. Schwartz had some news for his wife. "I'm reading the prison Bible and it's changing me."

His wife was pleased to hear that.

"Maybe that's why God gave me the judge I got," he added. "I never had time for religion before I was thrown in the slammer."

"God's ways are mysterious," his wife affirmed.

"When I get out of prison, I'm going to be a different man," R. B. said. He shared his plans, which made her very happy.

The guards indicated that it was time for them to say their goodbyes. The last words his wife said before she had to leave were, "I can hardly wait to take you home. I love you."

When his wife returned home, she told Dakota about the visit. "Your prayers for your father have paid off," she said.

"How so?" Dakota asked.

"You wanted God to give him a wake-up call—even if it meant God taking your life."

Dakota nodded.

"Your father is reading the Bible in his cell, and he wants to go to church with us when he gets out of prison." When she heard this news, Dakota could hardly contain her joy. "What's more," her mother added, "he says he wants to be rebaptized."

Tears ran down Dakota's cheeks. "God has answered my prayer. Now I can hope to see him in heaven."

Daddy Discovers Time for His Bible

"As drastic as it was," her mother said. "God had a better plan than you did. While it's pretty traumatic to spend time in jail, you'll admit it's better than God taking your life, Dakota."

Dakota heartily agreed. "God's way is best."

R. B. Schwartz was as good as his word. When he was released from prison, he arranged to be rebaptized and kept the Sabbath with his family. As time passed, he forgot all the pain of serving a prison sentence for a crime he didn't commit. Looking back, he knew that God's purpose was to save him for His kingdom.

Chapter 12

Midnight Gift

After the fireworks died down and the shouts grew hoarse, Craig MacLean dashed into his home, opened his refrigerator, grabbed a brown bag, ran to his neighbor's house, and rang the doorbell.

"Happy New Year!" Craig said when the door opened. "I saw your light was on, so I knew you were still up. I came over to give you this." He handed his neighbor the brown bag.

"I was planning to get drunk, but I just made my New Year's resolutions. I've decided to stop smoking and drinking tonight. Tomorrow's not only New Year's, it's a new decade—so it's the perfect time for me to quit. I've got to wait ten years for this opportunity to roll around again. I want to be a nurse, but I won't be able to keep a job unless I shake this alcoholic monkey off my back."

Craig pointed to the bag. "That's a bottle of poor man's brew. I want you to keep it because I know you're a pastor, so you won't touch it. I'd trash it, but I know myself too well! If I opened this bottle now, I'm so weak that I'd just pour it down my throat. I want to quit now, not tomorrow! Pray for me, Pastor, I'm joining Alcoholics Anonymous."

The pastor promised to put Craig on his prayer list, took the bottle gladly, and stored it in the back of his own refrigerator. There it stayed for five whole months.

On June 1, Craig sheepishly told the pastor he was still smoking because "AA advised me to quit one vice at a time." But he'd stayed dry five months and had learned of a job opportunity doing nursing in a retirement center. Craig asked the pastor to fill out a recommendation. The pastor happily obliged.

Midnight Gift

Later that night, the pastor got the bottle out of his refrigerator and took Craig outside on the back lawn. Craig shook the bottle, opened it, and waved it as the contents sprayed over the grass.

"I can honestly say, Pastor," Craig said after the last drop fell, "I no longer like the taste of alcohol. To me, that's a miracle. Thanks for your prayers. God must listen to you!"

But in the second week of October, Craig found himself battling hard against the desire for booze.

The first of October had been a wonderful day for him. He'd celebrated his ninth month of victory by sharing an ice cream cake with his boss.

Craig's boss owned two nursing homes. He'd been pleased that Craig had stayed dry for so long, so he'd given Craig a gift. Though it hadn't been gift wrapped, it had been Craig's dream come true. Craig had been promoted to manager.

Two weeks of management had been great. Great, that is, until the nurses' aides started quitting to attend college. Before he knew it, Craig discovered his help had been whittled down to two—a young African student and himself.

While the student was dependable and eager to work, she was somewhat deficient in the language. She did a good job, provided she understood what Craig said. Often, however, Craig found that it was easier just to do the task himself.

After putting in fifty-three hours in less than three days, Craig felt stress mounting. His old thirst returned. He didn't crave the taste; rather, he desired the euphoric release alcohol brought. He lit a cigarette to conquer the urge and inhaled deeply. He willed himself not to succumb.

Electrical problems compounded the issue. Craig called an electrician. Suddenly, Craig remembered HALT.

They'd discussed HALT at the previous AA meeting. HALT stood for Hungry, Angry, Lonely, Tired. If he were to stay dry and keep the respect of his boss and his employees, he had to pray. HALT was hitting him hard. If he prayed, he could resist, even though he was tired, frustrated, lonely, and hungry. Besides, all his friends were praying for him. He asked God to help him not to disappoint them.

As he was praying, the electrician arrived. Craig showed him the problem, and he was done in an hour. In the path of duty, the electrician heard Craig mumble, "Will this never end?"

"It'll pass," the electrician told Craig. "I don't blame you for doing everything yourself. Sometimes it seems it's a waste of time training aides because they quit on you a few months later. But don't worry!" He smiled at Craig. "It'll pass. I know what you're going through. I've been there."

"I've lost most of my workers." Craig hoped he didn't look as tired as he felt. But the electrician's words soothed his nerves. "I don't know where to find good help."

"What've you done so far?"

"Advertising. Notes on bulletin boards." Craig lit another cigarette to soothe his craving. "I've done everything."

"You'll find someone." He patted Craig on the back.

Craig's shoulders seemed to grow taller. This problem would resolve itself, and no bottle could help him gain a better edge. As Craig made his rounds after the electrician left, he prayed for a solution soon.

A college student came for a job interview. Craig was impressed with her but didn't think she really wanted to do nursing. Her talents lay in being a receptionist.

After she left, he donned his denim jacket, hopped into his pickup, and drove to the girls' dormitory. He hand delivered a recommendation for the student to work as a telephone operator. He told the dean about her and about his need for nurses.

"Why don't you call this number?" the girls' dean said. "Ask for Amanda. She's a nurse. If she wants work, she'd be great!"

Craig took the number, thanked the dean, and hurried off to join his evening support group at Alcoholics Anonymous. In the meeting he was shocked. Many of his peers had lied. They confessed that they'd been light social drinkers, off and on, for several months. They admitted they had *not* licked their problem. Their confessions smacked Craig right between his metaphoric eyes.

A little voice reminded Craig about his favorite corner in a quiet bar. Wasn't it too hard to resist every day? Once an alcoholic, always an alcoholic. His buddies knew the truth. He was just fooling himself. A working man under such a strain as he deserved a good drink.

Craig resisted the voice and the impulse to condemn his buddies. He felt disappointed, though, for their stories discouraged him. If he could stay dry, why couldn't they? Prayer must make a difference. Ironically, he found their failure strengthened him. It somehow made his own choice stronger.

He left the meeting early, drove straight home, took from his pocket the crumpled note bearing Amanda's phone number, and dialed. A woman's voice answered on the second ring.

"Hello, Amanda, what were you doing before you answered the phone?" Craig asked politely.

"You won't believe this," Amanda answered, "it may sound crazy to you, but I was on my knees praying someone would call and offer me a job!"

"Well, what time can you come for an interview? I have a job opening and I was praying you'd fill it!" Amanda and Craig met in his office at the retirement home. He interviewed her and she filled out an application. They signed a contract, and she began work immediately. Craig was exuberant, for much of his pressure was off. He thanked God for the chance to get the rest he needed in order to resist temptation.

Two days later an Indian nurse volunteered to work for free to demonstrate her competence. He started her on the Saturday afternoon shift as a volunteer and hired her on Monday.

Tuesday night Craig saw the pastor's light on. He shared the story with him. "My self-confidence is at an all-time high! I keep telling myself if I can make it through this kind of pressure, I'm not going to crack. My confidence improves employee and boss relations. I can look employees straight in the eye, and they know I can handle tough times without resorting to crutches." Craig invited the pastor to eat some German chocolate cake on New Year's to celebrate his one-year anniversary of being dry.

When Craig left the pastor's house, he prayed that come New Year's Eve, he'd be strong enough to continue waging the battle against booze and to snuff out his last cigarette.

It's been over twenty years since Craig had his last drink and smoked his last cigarette. He praises God for transforming him into a recovered alcoholic after wasting eighteen years of his life trying to escape in a bottle.

Chapter 13

Thanksgiving Shoes

Pedal, pedal, pedal, *scraaaaaaaape*! Pedal, pedal, pedal, *scraaaaaaaape*!

Eric rode his bike as fast as he could down the curving road that led to his home. When he felt that he couldn't push the pedal a second longer, or that he was going at a speed that made him uncomfortable, Eric, while still sitting on his bicycle seat, slammed his shoes onto the pavement, coasting on them until the bike came to a complete stop. Lifting his feet back onto the pedals, he repeated the process.

Pedal, pedal, pedal, *scraaaaaaaape*! Pedal, pedal, pedal, *scraaaaaaaape*!

As he turned a bend in the road with his shoes sliding against the pavement, he slowly passed Stanley,* a classmate who was walking home from school. When the bicycle came to a stop a few feet ahead of Stanley, he said, "Hey, Eric, you're gonna wear out your shoes if you keep sliding 'em on the road like that!"

"That's exactly what I want!"

"What?" Stanley said incredulously. "You want a pair of shoes with no souls?"

"Very funny!" Eric made a fake laugh. "Soul-less shoes—as if they have a heart! Yeah, I wanna wear out my shoes," Eric replied.

"Why?" Stanley asked. "It'd be such a waste. Those shoes look pretty good."

"Good!" Eric shouted. "Good! These are hand-me-down shoes. I hate hand-me-down shoes!"

"Those are hand-me-down shoes?" Stanley asked. "I'd never've guessed."

---

* The author, Stanley M. Maxwell—a.k.a. Mr. Stan—plays a minor role in this story; however, the other characters' names, and the places and events have been disguised to protect the innocent.

70

Thanksgiving Shoes

"Shows what you know!" Eric sneered as he brushed his shoes along the pavement. "They're worse than hand-me-down shoes," he griped. "These are hand-me-down secondhand shoes."

"You've gotta be kidding."

"Nope, I kid you not."

"How so?"

"There are five of us kids in the family—Earl; Eddie; me; my sister, Esther; and my baby brother, Ethan."

"You've got a big family," Stanley conceded.

"Well, my oldest brother, Earl, always gets the new shoes. When he outgrows them, my parents give them to Eddie, and then, when Eddie is too big, the clothes come down to me, so they're twice owned before I get 'em."

"I see." Stanley nodded.

"Hand-me-down clothes are bad enough," Eric continued, "but it won't stop with me."

"Oh?"

"Yea, after I'm through with them, they get passed onto my poor little brother, Ethan."

"So, you gotta keep these shoes nice for Ethan as Earl and Eddie did for you," Stanley said. "What's he gonna do if you wear them out?"

"No, you knucklehead! You don't get it!" Eric exclaimed. "Earl gets new clothes—just because he's the eldest. And Esther, because she's the only girl, always gets new clothes, but I, the middle child, never do. And neither do Eddie and Ethan. It's just not fair—why can't I get new clothes once in a while? Of course, I know, it's worse for Ethan than it is for me—my kid brother has to wear hand-me-down, hand-me-down, secondhand shoes. I feel so sorry for him! But why do I have to wear hand-me-down secondhand shoes?"

"I wish I knew," Stanley confessed.

"Well, I have a plan, Stan." Eric had gotten off the bike and was now pushing it as he walked with Stanley.

"What's that?" Stanley asked.

"I want to wear out my shoes before Thanksgiving," Eric exclaimed. "Then my parents will have to give me a new pair by the third Thursday of November when we have our big family get-together. New shoes will give me something to be thankful for."

"So if you get something, then you can be thankful on Thanksgiving."

"Duh," Eric said. "It's Thanksgiving—the day you're thankful for what you get."

"You're giving me some new ideas," Stanley said thoughtfully. "Here I thought you were supposed to be thankful for what you already have."

"I can't be thankful for something I hate, now can I?" Eric shouted as he kicked his shoes against his bicycle tire.

"I never thought of it that way," Stanley mused.

"I think a lot," Eric twisted his mouth into his lopsided smile as he turned into his driveway. He hopped onto his bike, rode it into the garage, parked it, and then waved goodbye to Stanley, who walked another half block to his own home.

Over the next few weeks, Eric carried out his plan diligently until the soles came loose and flapped. Soon his classmates were commenting about them on the playground. "Hey, Eric, were you made upside down?"

"No," Eric retorted.

"Your feet have a mouth and the tongue inside smells—and now your eyes and nose are running," some taunted. "See, you are made upside down."

"You got it all wrong," Eric retorted. "My shoes have a personality of their own. When I walk, they talk."

Hearing it put that way, the schoolmates changed their attitude, "Cool, man," they said and left him alone.

When Eric arrived home from school, he pranced around his house in his floppy shoes looking for his mother, who, when he found her, noticed his shoes immediately. "Oh, Eric," she sighed. "Look what you've done to your shoes!" Eric wiped the smile off his face and cowered in anticipation. "What is it about you, Eric? Earl can wear his shoes and keep them almost like new, and they weren't bad when Eddie got them, but now look at them. Money doesn't grow on trees! Not when you have to think of putting five children in Christian schools like your father and I do. We have to make every penny count!"

When his mother finished, Eric slunk off to his room, slammed the door, and flopped on his bed, uncertain whether he should sulk, explode, or weep. Wallowing in self-pity, he felt life was so unfair. It seemed now that he'd have to wear his floppy shoes until they were too small. He wasn't excited with the prospect of Ethan's getting that new pair of shoes he'd wanted for himself.

Thanksgiving Shoes

The days grew colder as Thanksgiving neared. Outside, snow piled up as the wind chilled whatever it touched, and the temperature dropped below zero. Eric had forgotten how shoes keep feet warm. Still his parents didn't take him shopping for new ones. In desperation, he decided to fix them. Finding duct tape in the basement, he wrapped it around his shoes. *At least my feet will be warm,* he consoled himself, but he dreaded going to school in the morning.

Indeed, the next day, as he walked the school halls, one of his classmates jeered, "Hey, nice tape! Were your shoes talkin' too much?"

Another laughed, "Were those shoes gettin' noisy—is that why you taped 'em shut? Do they keep you up at night? Yackity yack yack, don't talk back!"

Very funny, Eric thought sarcastically to himself.

Someone else sneered, "Why don't your parents just buy you a new pair?"

Eric felt he had no choice but to endure the taunts from his classmates. *It's all my fault,* he reasoned bitterly to himself. *I should've picked better parents before I was floating in the womb!* Somehow he made it through the school day, then dashed down the snow-covered road that led home as fast as his duct-taped shoes would let him. He was racing to his room when his mother called.

Reluctantly he turned around and faced his mother, then sheepishly looked down at his shoes, hoping she would notice them. She didn't.

"Eric," Mother said, "it's time for our family tradition around Thanksgiving time." They liked to drive to some of the farms in the area and visit the migrant workers to see if there was anything they needed. "There's enough room in the car for one friend. Who would you like to invite?"

"I'll think about it, Mother," Eric said and disappeared into his room and picked up the phone.

Eric asked Stanley to come along. Wallowing in unrepentant self-inflicted misery, he loathed the annual trip to the farms to visit the farm workers. *Blessed be company,* he thought. Happily, having Stanley along would put him on his best behavior; talking with him, he knew, would help him forget about his troubles. He felt comfortable with Stanley because he hadn't made fun of his shoes. They all crowded into their old station wagon and drove off to country roads, past vineyards and orchards, and turned down a farm road that led to an old wooden shack.

Stopping the car in front of the shack, his parents jumped out and knocked on the door. The rest of the family and Stanley followed and stood politely behind the parents as they waited for the door to open.

When it did, a handsome black man stood in the doorway wearing a broad welcoming smile. "Come inside," he beckoned with a wave of his hand.

Mother and Dad, Earl and Eddie, Esther and Ethan, Eric and Stanley packed in. The shack was well heated with a Franklin wood stove. They opened their host's cupboards and stared in disbelief at the empty shelves. Meanwhile, Eric and Stanley noticed the man's bare feet.

Just as Eric was beginning to feel claustrophobic, his mother announced, "We're going shopping, and when we return, these shelves will be filled with food." Beaming with gratitude, the man enthusiastically shook hands with each of his guests.

Everyone stepped out of the heated shack into the cold. The barefoot man strode quickly through the snow to the car and opened the doors like a chauffeur. He waved as it drove off.

Eric sat quietly in the back seat with his brows furrowed in thought. "Mother," he spoke up finally.

"Yes, Eric," Mother replied.

"Did you notice the man's shoes?" Eric asked.

"You're still thinking about shoes," Mother sighed. "We can't afford shoes right now."

"I know, Mother," Eric said. "I get that. But I've been thinking about that man. He didn't have any shoes! At least I have a pair—oh yeah, they were floppy and they have a personality of their own; now they're duct-taped and they make me the laughingstock in the school halls. But they're still shoes. They can keep my feet warm. That man walks barefoot in the snow! Did you know that?"

"What are you trying to say?" Daddy asked.

"Well, I was thinking about my duct-taped shoes and his bare feet in the snow," Eric said. "I've come up with an idea."

"What's that?" Mother asked.

"I know you said you couldn't buy me a new pair of shoes." Eric's voice initially sounded timid then grew bolder. "It's my fault they've worn out early, so I don't deserve new shoes, but what about this man? He needs shoes! Just forget that I ever asked for new ones—please, buy him a pair instead! Let's take him to the mall and let him pick out a good pair."

"That's a wonderful idea," said Daddy.

Thanksgiving Shoes

"It's the most unselfish thing I've heard you say in a long time." Mother beamed as she looked into the rearview mirror to see Eric's face. "We'll make arrangements for him to buy a pair of shoes in the mall."

"May I go with you when you take him to the shoe store?" Eric asked.

"It was your idea," Mother said.

"I don't see why not," Daddy added.

"May I take Stanley with me?" Eric asked.

"If he wants to come," Mother replied.

Eric turned toward his friend sitting beside him. "Do you want to, Stanley?" Stanley nodded his head.

"Then it's settled," Daddy exclaimed. "We'll do it. I'll call your mother, Stanley, and make arrangements for a time when you can come along."

And that's exactly what they did.

Stanley accompanied Eric and his parents down to the farm where the migrant worker lived. They picked him up, took him to the mall, and let him pick out a brand-new pair of tennis shoes at a discount store. The boys were delighted to see the happy look on the man's face as he walked from the mall wearing his new shoes. As they drove the man back to his shack, it seemed that he couldn't thank Eric and his family enough.

As the days drew nearer to Thanksgiving, Eric forgot about his duct-taped shoes. His friends grew accustomed to them and stopped teasing him. He felt happy about helping the farm worker get a pair of shoes for winter. However, at the dawn of Thanksgiving, Eric didn't feel so thankful. The day reminded him that his parents hadn't given him the new shoes he wanted.

Thanksgiving was a big event for Eric's family. All his uncles and aunts and cousins descended upon their house for the holiday. Mother prepared a feast for everyone. The table needed to be extended to enable the whole family to sit around it. Daddy was busy pulling the wooden dining room table apart so he could add all three leaves. Out came the embroidered table cloth followed by the cranberry sauce, stuffed Tofurky, tartar sauce, sweet potatoes, vegetables, a variety of pies, and much more. Around the Tofurky were carved turkeys made from baby carrots and radishes. Still more was being prepared in the kitchen.

All the commotion was too much for Eric, who lapsed into thinking about his secondhand shoes again. He feared what he'd say when the family, seated all around the table, would be asked to share something for which they were thankful. Off to his room he went to set up his Hot Wheels race tracks.

Eric was so absorbed in calculating the race that when Mother banged the dinner gong, he didn't hear it. He heard it the third time and reluctantly cleared up his set and sauntered down the hall toward the dining room. When he entered the dining room he saw all the food on the table with his family sitting around it. Everyone was watching him expectantly.

Then he saw it.

On his plate (it had to be his as it was the only seat not taken) was a wrapped package with a large golden bow. Puzzled, he sat down and stared at it.

"Open it," someone suggested.

Eric carefully lifted the tape on the wrapping paper in an effort to save it for reuse.

"Hurry up!" Ethan said, "I'm hungry!"

Vigorously tearing off the remaining wrap, Eric tossed it onto the floor. Inside he saw a shoebox, but experience had taught him to look first before making assumptions about the contents. Cautiously, he lifted the lid.

"Oh," Eric gasped when he looked inside. There—he could scarcely believe his eyes—was a pair of shoes. The exact pair he'd longed for. "Thank you, Mother and Daddy!"

"After you offered to give up your shoes for the farm hand we visited who didn't even own any shoes," his mother said, "we thought that you'd learned such a valuable lesson that you deserved some new shoes yourself."

"Today is such a special day!" Eric exclaimed. "This is a Thanksgiving I'll never forget!"

And you know, from that day to this, he never did.

Chapter 14

The Man Who Rode to California on a Potato

Mother was cross. "Johnny," she said, "why on earth do you make the potatoes so small when you peel them?"

"I hate peeling these dumb, tiny potatoes with this stupid old knife," he complained. "I wish somebody would develop a *big* potato, as big as—as big as one of those dinosaur bones found on Britain's shores—or maybe as big as a bloated beached blue whale off the coast of Boston!"

Johnny lived in the 1860s, when big potatoes hadn't yet been developed. Potatoes then were very small, and that's why Johnny hated to peel them.

"Do you want to eat the potato skins?" Johnny protested.

"John Jonathan Johnson, don't be rude," Mrs. Johnson warned.

At the very time when Johnny was grumbling to his mother, it just so happened that Lute, another boy, who was wishing he could go to California, was about to fulfill Johnny's wish for a larger potato.

Lute grew potatoes. He was out in his potato field one day inspecting his plants when he saw on one of them a little round white ball. The ball was a seed pod—something very rare among potato plants. At once he became excited, for he knew that potato seeds don't make plants like the adults that produce them. Farmers who grow potatoes don't plant potato seeds. Instead, they take some of the previous year's potatoes, cut them up, and plant the pieces. These pieces grow into plants with new potatoes on the roots, and the new potatoes are just like the potato that was cut into pieces.

"Now," said Lute to himself, "with these seeds I can make a new kind of potato, maybe one that isn't so small. Maybe I'll even get a plant that grows big potatoes. And maybe for selling my new, big potatoes, I can get enough money to go to California." He knew he'd have to wait at least a year.

Lute kept the seed pod indoors all winter and the following spring planted the seeds. Twenty-three plants grew. When the plants were ready, he stuck in his fork to dig up the first one. Up came the ugliest potato he had ever seen—all wrinkled—and it didn't taste good either. After digging up twenty-one more plants and finding them all the same, he was reluctant to dig up the last one. He was shaking so much that the fork would hardly go into the ground, but when he got it in, he couldn't get it out. He thought it had gotten stuck on a rock or something, so he pulled a little harder and out it came. Something *was* stuck on it. He looked closely and found it was not a rock, but the biggest potato he'd ever seen in his whole life! He and his mother took it in and ate it. It was the most delicious potato they'd ever eaten.

Lute took cuttings of the plant, and soon he had a big bag full of his large, smooth, delicious potatoes. He was able to sell the rights to this type of potato to a nurseryman for $150! By the time Lute left town for California there were thousands of big potatoes.

Now Johnny couldn't grumble anymore. For Lute—or Luther Burbank as he is generally known—had fulfilled Johnny's wish by taking the smallness out of potatoes, and at the same time he'd fulfilled his own wish to go to California.

So we could say that Luther Burbank is the man who "rode to California on a potato!"

Chapter 15

The "Saving Fields" in Thailand

When I was a college student during President Jimmy Carter's administration, I was impressed when the First Lady visited starving Khmer refugees. I came to understand their suffering a little better after watching the movie *The Killing Fields,* a story about a Cambodian journalist who survived the Khmer Rouge genocide to report the atrocities. Clearly these Southeast Asians deserved help. I wanted to turn the "killing fields" into a "saving field." I decided I wanted to work for refugees when I graduated. I hoped, for the refugees' sake, there wouldn't be any refugees then, but I wanted to help if there were still a problem. After I graduated, I discovered that the refugee problem, though no longer in the news, was far from solved.

Vietnam was at war on the Thai-Kampuchea border every dry season, attempting to destroy the last strongholds of the Khmer People's National Liberation Front. Because of the fighting, many refugee camps were maintained in Thailand supported by Thailand's Ministry of Interior (MOI) and the UN High Commissioner for Refugees (UNHCR).

At every Hanoi offensive, some Vietnamese Communist soldiers deserted, rejecting Communism and requesting Thailand to accept them as refugees and help them to resettle in a Third Country (a term used in the context of migration designating a country accepting them as residents). The deserters were first debriefed in a jail at Aranyaprathet; then they were transferred to Panat Nikhom (PNK) Refugee Processing and Transit Center to live in the "Aran"

Section. Thailand hoped that Western embassy officials would interview the deserters and accept them for resettlement.

Initially, the defectors were largely ignored by embassies and suspected of being spies. They were discouraged from studying or working in the camp, thus perpetuating their ignorance and poverty.

A former Nationalist regiment commander, Nguyen Huu Chu, who, after Saigon's fall had been imprisoned by the Communists in a hard-labor camp for six years, came to PNK in September 1984 and agreed to assist me in the English language program I developed for the refugees. Chu hated Communists and initially dissuaded any students with suspected Communist thinking from taking my classes.

PNK is a refugee processing and transit camp and most refugees are processed to another camp or resettled in a Third Country quickly. Thus a typical student in my classes stayed no longer than two months. I liked students to stay longer so I could teach them more. I told Chu, "Recruit anyone staying in camp a long time." Chu thought of the Aran refugees—the Communist deserters. Rejected by every country, who'd stay longer than they? He said by trying to convert Arans to Christianity, we were fighting Communism, and he was "killing Communists without using bullets."

He told the former Communists that the Communist regime had brainwashed them during their time of duty, and now they must prove to embassy officials that they had reeducated. The best way to free their minds from Communism was to fill their minds with religious beliefs. The Seventh-day Adventist Church had the best religion and it welcomed them, he told them. "Come, learn from an American teacher about the West and how to speak English; understand Christian doctrines and be baptized into the Seventh-day Adventist Church."

My classes filled with between seventy to one hundred former Communist soldiers ages seventeen to thirty. I feared them. To be honest, I must admit that I wasn't sure they'd even be willing to learn about Christianity. They seemed hopeless, coming to class with shaved heads, cold eyes, and "impolite" tones of voice, according to Chu. During class some wrote or read letters, some slept, some talked to each other, some looked bored, some stared out the windows, some put their feet on the benches; most didn't pay much attention to me.

Every Friday after class, I announced, "Come to church tomorrow at two o'clock." One Friday after my usual speech, a student in the front row said, "Come to church to eat candy." (We offered candy or fruit and tea after church, as is the custom in Vietnam). I asked him, "Do you come to church to eat candy or to learn about God?" He answered, "To learn about God." I only half believed him.

A breakthrough came when least expected. My translator, Lam, a former businessman in Saigon, encouraged me to teach doctrines through Bible stories. "These soldiers have only third- or fourth-grade education," he explained. "They don't have the education to understand doctrines." The next day I told the story of Rahab, who helped the spies in Jericho. After the story, I said, "You're all former Communist soldiers. Probably each of you has done many evil things: lying, stealing, and killing." A few soldiers nodded their heads. "God accepted Rahab, a prostitute, and didn't kill her when Jericho fell, because she believed God. She changed and even became an ancestor of Jesus Christ, who died so you could be forgiven. If God can forgive a prostitute, who's considered by some as much lower then you in society, He can forgive and change you." A student stayed after class. Chu translated for him: "I didn't know God could forgive me and that I could become good," he said.

Gradually, I noticed a difference in class. The students looked happier, their expression in their eyes softened, their feet stayed off the benches. They smiled easily, were respectful to me, and seemed willing to help me in any way. I could trust their honesty.

Chu was baptized in June 1985, before he left. Baptisms occurred monthly after July until about seventy became regular church members. Ngan, a former Communist soldier, led our fifteen-member Aran church choir.

Nguyen Van Ngoc, a former sergeant, was baptized in February 1985. He was the church treasurer, and I trusted him with money as much as I trusted myself. Ngoc organized volunteers from the Aran congregation to build a bigger church with money from Thailand Mission.

In October 1985, my students Phuoc and Hieu—baptized former soldiers—became my class translators. But the next month, they and other new Adventists faced a test of loyalty. The Catholic Church started a sponsorship program to Canada and France for Aran refugees who accepted Catholicism. Phuoc and Hieu responded: "We cannot join the Catholics to be sponsored even though we want to go to Canada very badly. We're Seventh-day Adventists. If they sponsor us and we can go as Seventh-day Adventists, we'll go, but we can't give up the Sabbath and be Catholic just to be sponsored."

At my farewell party on February 4, 1986, which was also Ngoc's birthday, Phuoc and Hieu stated that they wished to meet me in the Third Country, but prayed that I'd meet them in the Fourth Country (heaven).

Chapter 16

From Sworn Enemies to Lifelong Friends

Part 1: The Spy Who Wasn't There

"Lackey!"

"Yes, Your Majesty!" The servant approached the Syrian king's bedside. "You called?"

"So we did." The king smiled. "We see you came rather quickly, which pleases us."

"Thank you, Your Highness." The servant beamed. "It pleases me to please you!"

The king turned his head from side to side as if he were looking for unseen eyes. Following the king's beckoning, the servant bent close to the monarch's ear. "We're afraid the walls have ears," the king whispered.

"Yes, Your Majesty," the servant replied, hoping he'd hid the puzzlement he felt.

"Can we—I—trust you?" the king asked.

Startled, the servant almost stammered. "Oh, indubitably, my king—you can trust me with your life!" To show his sincerity, the servant stood erect.

"We thought you might say that," the king sneered. He pondered momentarily then said, "No matter. We no longer know who is trustworthy in our court, but I must trust someone. Might as well be you."

"Yes, Your Majesty," the servant replied. "I'm honored, Sire! How can I be of assistance?"

"Come closer," the king beckoned. The servant obeyed. "Don't react suddenly to what we're about to say."

The servant nodded and placed his fingers to his lips to show they were sealed.

Satisfied, the king whispered, "We believe there's a spy in our court."

"A spy, Sire?" the shocked servant's voice boomed throughout the room.

"Quiet!" the king yelled as he looked nervously around the room again. "This must be kept secret."

"Oh, sorry, Sire. You startled me with your statement. It caught me completely off guard." The servant was whispering again, which calmed the king. "Seriously, a spy, Sire? Are you quite sure?"

"We're quite certain of it," the king intoned soberly.

"Have you any idea who it might be, Your Highness?"

"Perhaps in the military," the king answered.

"The military, Your Highness?" the servant replied. "Do you have any clues?"

"Our only clue is a strong suspicion based on repeated evidence."

"What evidence, Sire?" the servant asked.

"Well, every time we plan a battle to defeat our enemy Israel, whenever we arrive at the point of attack, Israel's king is already there with his army," the Syrian king explained as he stroked his beard. "How can that be—unless we have a spy among us reporting every word we say to the Israelite king?"

The servant audibly sighed with relief, "Your Majesty needn't worry about a spy in your court."

"No!" The king exploded then quieted down when he remembered the nature of the conversation. "No?"

"No, Your Highness. I can assure you, Sire, there is no spy *among us* who's aiding Israel." The servant smiled.

The king sat upright. "You mean you know who it is?"

"I'm surprised, O king, that you yourself don't know by now," his servant said soothingly.

"Then tell us!" exclaimed the king. "I hate being the last one to know things.

From Sworn Enemies to Lifelong Friends

I am king! It's your duty to keep me informed!"

"Of course, Your Majesty, I'll tell you."

"Who is it?" the king roared impatiently.

"It's well known, Your Majesty, that there's an Israelite who hears every secret you whisper," the servant said.

"He hears our whispers!" the king gasped.

"Yes, my Lord, every word you whisper in your bedchamber."

"Where is this Israelite?" the king demanded. "How can he hear what we whisper, if he isn't in our court somewhere?"

"He hears your whispers and divines your thoughts while he's enjoying the comforts of his very own home in Israel, Sire," the servant explained patiently.

"In Israel!" the king scoffed. "We don't believe you," he exploded. "This man you speak of, you say, hears what we say right here in my palace here in Damascus and—oh, our head is starting to hurt—and you want us to believe that this man never leaves his home in Israel! That this man can hear our whispers all the way over in Israel? Do you take us for a fool?"

"Yes, Sire, I—I mean no, Your Highness," the servant tripped over his tongue. "You're no fool, Your Majesty—you just don't see what I mean."

"That's impossible!" the king bellowed. "It can't be true!"

"Oh, but it *is* quite true, Your Highness!" The servant smiled. "Everyone in your court knows that Israel has a prophet—"

"A prophet, you say?" the king interrupted. "Bah! What do prophets know? Our prophets just say sweet words that make us feel happy. They don't know anything really."

"Ah, that may be true, Your Highness, but *this* prophet is quite different," the servant said tactfully.

"Quite different, you say?" the king asked.

"Yes, different, my Lord."

"How's he different?" The servant had the king's rapt attention.

"This prophet in Israel knows every word you speak—even in the privacy of your bedchamber—because his God tells him of your plans to harm His people," the servant spoke authoritatively. "This prophet then reports God's messages directly to the king of Israel."

"Who knows beforehand exactly where we will strike next and then prepares!"

The servant nodded. "I think you're starting to see what I mean."

The king had a faraway look in his eyes as if he were plotting another one of his regal schemes. "So, you say that this prophet knows everything that we say—even in our bedchamber?"

"Yes, O king," the servant replied.

"And this prophet tells my words to the king of Israel?"

"That's what I said, Your Majesty," the servant intoned.

"That's what we were afraid you said," the king's voice sounded distant. "Then the king of Israel has no spies in our court?"

"Precisely," the servant replied. "Why *would* he need spies, Your Highness, when he's got a prophet *outside* your court who's telling him everything he needs to know?"

"Yes, we see," the king leaped from his bed and stood on the floor. "Dress us for court!" he ordered.

The servant obeyed.

"Bring us our robe." The king extended his arms and the servant draped the robe around the king. "We must have our signet ring, our crown, and our scepter. Prepare them."

"As you wish, my Lord," the servant cocked his head as he replied. Soon he returned bringing the items the king had requested.

"Accompany us to court," the king ordered. "We would speak with you on the way."

The servant did as he was told. As the two walked toward the king's courtroom, the king asked his servant, "Would we be right to assume that the Israelite king would know *none* of our plans if it weren't for the word of this prophet?"

"Yes, Your Highness," the servant nodded. "It appears so, Sire."

"That's good," the king said as he entered his court and sat upon his throne. "How do we look?"

"You appear most regal, Sire." The servant stood guard at the king's right side.

"Quite! Then all is in readiness." With a wave of his hand, the king proclaimed, "You may call the court to order."

"Yes, Your Majesty." The servant bowed.

"See to it now," ordered the king, "Without delay!"

"Attention! Attention!" the servant bellowed once the courtiers had assembled. "All ears attend the king who is now in court. Court is in session and your presence is mandatory by order of his Royal Majesty, the king! Long live the king!"

In came all the courtiers, each dressed in his finest. The princes, the soothsayers, the wise men, the councilors, and the generals all took their places. Some of them bore gifts to curry favor with the king. All bore pompous airs that seemed to say that the world couldn't function were they not in it. To all appearances, they touted their importance and rank with every step they took.

"Bow the knee! Bow the knee!" the servant cried. The king watched as all of the members of his court bowed low before him, declaring dutifully, "Long live the king! Long live the king!" As their noses scraped the floor, the king tipped his head approvingly. With a slight wave of his hand, he looked to his servant, who'd been awaiting the signal.

"All rise! All rise!" the servant declared.

When the courtiers had risen to their feet, the servant proclaimed, "His Majesty, the great and mighty king of Syria, wishes to speak!"

The king rose from his throne and looked over his court. "We're told that the king of Israel knows every word we say, even the secret words we speak in our bedchamber. He knows all that we plan because a prophet tells him. Is this true, General?"

The general stepped forward and bowed respectfully, "It is, my Lord, the king!"

"Does anyone know where this prophet lives?" the king's eyes bore into the general's.

"I do, Your Majesty," said the general.

"Where?" the king demanded. "Out with it!"

"In Dothan, Your Highness," the general answered and bowed.

"Is the city of Dothan fortified?" the king asked.

"No, my Lord," the general replied as he tipped his head. "It is not."

"And is it true that without the counsel of this prophet, the king of Israel would know *nothing* of our plans?" the king asked.

A councilor stepped forward and bowed. "O, king, live forever."

The king tipped his scepter toward the man and said, "Speak, councilor."

"It's our opinion, oh king, that without this prophet, the Israelite king would know none of your plans," the councilor advised.

"Then, would you say that without this prophet, we could fight Israel and defeat them?" the king asked.

"That is our conclusion, Your Highness," the councilor replied.

"Then the solution seems simple," the king declared. "General!"

"Yes, Your Majesty." The general bowed.

"How long would it take you to assemble the horses and the chariots and the army?"

After pondering a moment, the general told him.

"Then do so immediately," the king ordered.

"What's our mission, Sire?" the general asked.

"We'll march to Dothan, capture this prophet, whoever he is," the king waved his hand, "and take him to Syria, where we can keep a close eye on him." The king's mouth spread into a devious smile. "Then we'll see how prepared the king of Israel is for our next attack!"

"Yes, Your Majesty!" the general declared. "Immediately, Sire!"

"See that you do!" the king admonished.

"I'll see it through personally, Your Highness. You have my word, Sire," the general cried. "I'll keep an eye on every detail of the preparation, Sire, to be quite sure that it's planned perfectly."

"That's what we want to hear!" the king intoned. "Now go!"

"Well planned, Your Highness!" said the councilor after the general had departed.

"Of course it was," the king said. "We see what to do and act upon it. That's why we're the king!" Turning toward his servant he said, "Court is dismissed!"

Instantly the servant shouted, "Court is dismissed! Bow the knee! Bow the knee!"

The members of the court proceeded to step backward, bowing as they slowly made their way from the courtroom. Keeping their eyes steadily upon the king, the members dutifully declared, "Long live the king! Long live the king!"

Part 2: Seeing What Was Once Unseen

Sometime later, in Dothan, a student of the Israelite prophet looked out the upper window of his master's home and nearly froze in midstride. Panicked, he dashed to the prophet's room. "Master," he called frantically, "come quickly! I want to show you something!"

"What is it, my son?" asked the prophet kindly. "Calm down and tell me what's troubling you."

"Come quickly," the student replied. "It's best you see this for yourself. We'll need to act swiftly."

"Show me the way," the prophet said as he got up. "I'll follow."

The student led his master to the window, pointed, and exclaimed nervously, "Look, master, we're surrounded by the Syrian army!" Turning to his master, he was surprised to see that the prophet had remained calm. "Don't you think we need to plan our escape? I'm pretty sure the Syrian army is here to capture you because you tell our king whatever the Syrian king thinks and plans against Israel." The student looked all around him and then cried out fearfully, "It may be too late already! The city's completely surrounded with horses, chariots, and a host of Syrian soldiers! What shall we do, master?"

"We're not going to try to escape, son," the prophet answered.

"You're not even worried?" the student said in surprise.

"We've got nothing to worry about, my son."

"Nothing to worry about!" exclaimed the student. "Master, we're surrounded by the entire army of the king of Syria with his horses and his chariots—and you say we have nothing to worry about. You're either braver than I thought, or—"

"My son, there are more with us than there are with them!"

"What do you mean, master?" the student said. "When I consider all your students and even all those living in Dothan, the host surrounding us is much greater. I don't see why you're not worried, master."

"You don't see what I see," the prophet sighed patiently. "Obviously, you don't look at things the way I do," he mused as he stroked his beard. "Well, it appears we'll have to do something about that, son. After all, this is the school of the prophets."

"What do you see, master?" the student asked.

"Do you want to be a seer?" the master asked.

"That's one reason why I joined the school of the prophets and became your student," he said earnestly to his master. "Yes, I desire to be a seer very much!"

"Good!" Looking up toward heaven, the master spread his hands and prayed,

"Lord, open the eyes of this student that he might see!"

"Oh, I see now!" exclaimed the student. "God has sent an army of angels with chariots and horses to protect us!"

"Thank You, Lord, for answering my prayer," said the prophet. Turning to his student, the master said, "Now you see what is unseen."

"Yes, master!" the student said excitedly. "The heavenly host, with its horses and chariots, is far larger and mightier than all the Syrian host."

"That's right, my son." The master placed his hand on the student's shoulder and smiled reassuringly. "Always remember: There are two good angels for every evil one. If we're on God's side, those who are for us outnumber those who are against us."

"I see," said the student. "What do we do now, master?"

"I'm going to pray," the prophet replied. Again he looked up toward heaven and extended his hand. "Lord God of Israel," he began then pointed his hand toward the Syrian army. "Smite them with blindness that they may not see."

"Look, master," the student cried once he had opened his eyes after the prophet had finished his prayer. "It appears that God has answered your prayer. See, the Syrian army is groping around as if in darkness."

"God has removed their sight," the prophet confirmed.

"It would be funny if it weren't so serious," the student said, mindful that at the request of his master, God had opened his eyes but had blinded the Syrian army. "Look how they're falling over each other and leaning on each other for support."

"My son, I think the Syrian general and his army could use our assistance," the prophet said. "With our help, they'll soon be able to see much better."

"I don't see what you mean—"

"You'll see, soon enough," the prophet interrupted. "Things appear a little murky at the moment for you, I know, my son, but you'll see much today. Eventually you'll see everything clearly." The prophet flashed his student a contagious smile. When the student shook his head and returned a puzzled smile, the prophet urged, "Come! Let's go down now, my son, and discover their intentions." With that, the prophet walked down the steps and hurried down the road toward the Syrian army. His bewildered student, still shaking his head, followed his master out the city gate.

Once outside the city, the prophet shouted to the army, "Whom do you seek?"

From Sworn Enemies to Lifelong Friends

A soldier turned toward the voice, and yelled, "What'd you say?"

"I said, 'Whom do you seek?' "

"I'm not sure," answered the soldier as he groped toward the prophet. Then he turned to the soldier beside him and asked, "Whom do we seek?"

"Ask the general," the second soldier replied. "I'm quite sure he knows. He organized this expedition."

"Good idea!" exclaimed the first soldier. "How do we find him in all this darkness?"

"Call out to him until he answers and finds you," the second soldier suggested.

"Let's call together," said the first soldier. "There's a higher chance that he'll hear us and come our way." So they called out to the general until one of the king's servants helped lead him to the soldiers who'd spoken with the prophet. When he eventually arrived, the soldiers told the general, "Someone asked whom we seek, sir."

"Where is this man of whom you speak?" the general answered. "I cannot see him."

"I'm here, sir," called the prophet. "Tell me, sir, whom do you seek?"

Turning toward the direction of the voice, the general said, "I think you know whom we seek."

"Follow me, General, I'll take you to whom you seek," said the prophet, basing his answer upon what he'd seen in vision. "Command your horses and chariots and your mighty host to come with me."

"You know where I can find him?"

"Follow me and you'll see him," Elisha said.

"How shall we find him?" the king asked. "Having just lost our sight, we cannot see how to follow you."

Elisha replied, "This isn't the way, sir, neither is this the city: follow me, and I'll bring you to the man whom you seek." The prophet asked his servant to line up the Syrian army so that they were touching each other's shoulders and could march in line as they followed the prophet. Elisha then led the army away from his hometown of Dothan to Samaria, the Israelite capital at that time.

The Israelite king opened the Samarian gates, and Elisha, along with the Syrian army and its horses and chariots, entered. The gates slammed shut behind them.

"I still don't see what your plan is, master," the student said.

"Watch," replied Elisha. "You'll see." The prophet lifted his eyes toward heaven and spread his arms. "Lord, God of Israel, please open the eyes of these men that they may see."

God heard the prophet's prayer and returned sight to the army of Syria. When they looked around them, they trembled with fear. They saw that they were inside the walls of Samaria and surrounded by the army of Israel. "Blindsided! That's how I feel!" the general protested. "You've betrayed us into the hand of the king of Israel. Who are you anyway?"

"Who'd you say you were looking for?" the prophet asked.

"To see the prophet Elisha, from Dothan," the general snapped.

"Well, I am he!" the prophet said puzzled. "Wait—*I'm* the one you seek? You sought me—Elisha?"

"You tricked us!" cried the general angrily. "Your voice sounds like the man who led us here from Dothan."

"I didn't trick you," Elisha explained. "The God of Israel revealed to me that you wanted to see the Israelite king. That's why I brought you to Samaria."

"Well," the general snorted, "our king changed his plans. Didn't your God inform you of that also?"

"No," Elisha replied. "It appears that God shows me things on a need-to-know basis. I see that I didn't need to know you were looking for me."

"Well, now you know we wanted to see Elisha, that prophet at Dothan who shares the Syrian king's battle plans with the king of Israel," the general snapped.

"Now you see me," Elisha said.

"Yeah, we see you all right. We see you for what kind of man you really are," the general sneered suspiciously. "Men," the general turned to his army and declared in his own language, "it appears to me that this may be our last day. If so, all of Syria will view it as a day of infamy!"

Turning to Elisha, the general said, "Now that you've trapped us in Samaria, what's to become of us?"

"Yes," laughed the king of Israel, who was rubbing his hands in gleeful anticipation. He came down and stood beside Elisha. "What shall we do with the Syrians? Shall I kill them?"

"No, Your Highness," the prophet shook his head. "Bring them bread and water and send them on their merry way home to their master the king of Syria."

From Sworn Enemies to Lifelong Friends

"Feed them!" the king shouted angrily. "You've got a strange point of view, Elisha! Whose side are you on anyway?"

"God's side, Your Majesty," Elisha replied.

"Of course," the king nodded then glared. "Well, the way I see it," the Israelite king retorted, "I should take advantage of this opportunity to kill them all right now. The Syrians are nothing but trouble for me! Why should I feed them?"

"You'll see, Sire," the prophet intoned. "I think that if you do, Your Majesty, you'll look back and see it as perhaps one of the best investments you ever made."

"Oh, I see," the king's eyes brightened. "Perhaps you're onto something, Elisha," he mused. "Well," he began excitedly, "if we're going to feed this great host of Syria, we'll see to it that they have a feast that they'll never forget!" He called to his lackey, "Tell my personal chef to look for enough food to feed the entire army of Syria, not to mention my entire court. I want the finest figs, olives, pomegranates, lentils, and chickpeas. And of course we'll need meat from the fattest animals." The lackey dashed off to find the royal chef. The king ordered other servants to look after the tables for the feast.

Indeed, it was a feast to remember. The Israelites and the Syrians sat looking eye to eye as they dined to their hearts' content. Then the Israelite king, following Elisha's request, sent the Syrian general and his horses and his chariots and his vast host back to their master in Damascus. The feast must have helped the Syrians see things in a new light as well, for it was said that for the rest of the reigns of those two kings, neither saw each other in battle again.

Later, after Israel and Syria had enjoyed years of peace, Elisha's student reflected, "I see your point of view now, master. On that day that the Israelite king, at your suggestion, served a banquet to the Syrian army, he killed his sworn enemies with kindness and transformed them into lifelong friends."

Elisha nodded and smiled.

Chapter 17

Miracles in Unexpected Places!

I held my food tray in my hand, scanning the school cafeteria for an empty table as I wasn't in the mood to join a group that might be nearly finished eating and leave as soon as I arrived. A group arose, vacating a table, and I headed for it. When I began eating, I saw my roommate, Kyle, heading in my direction. He flopped into his chair and slouched over his food. After halfheartedly picking at his mashed potatoes and gravy, he declared, "Hi! I'm depressed."

"Any way I can help you get over your depression?" I offered.

"Not anymore."

"What?" I asked.

Kyle must've used his peripheral vision because he announced, "Look over at two o'clock and see who's coming our way." He gave me a big grin. If I'd doubted his recovery from depression I was now convinced because the medicine was walking our way in the form of a petite brunette wearing blue jeans and a red-plaid flannel shirt.

"How do you get so many girls to sit with you during lunch?" I teased. "Every time you come to eat with me, a different girl joins us."

"That's easy," Kyle replied. "I take nursing classes."

"Why?" I wrinkled my forehead in puzzlement. "You've told me repeatedly that you want to be a certified public accountant like your dad. Did you change your mind?"

"No," he said, "I still want to account for myself by adding long lists of

Miracles in Unexpected Places!

numbers. I'll major in accounting."

"So why the nursing classes?" I asked, still baffled. "How will nursing classes help with accounting?"

"What's one thing you're certain to have in nursing classes?"

"Let me guess, um, a lot of difficult scientific words to memorize and understand—sort of like learning a foreign language?"

"Close," my roommate laughed, "but you missed it by a mile."

"I give up!"

"Girls!" Kyle explained. "I take nursing classes to meet girls. For some reason if you're a guy in their class, you're somehow approachable. Watch," he said. "She'll join us, I'm certain."

Apprehensive that if I looked in her direction I might appear too eager and chase her away, I watched with my peripheral vision as the girl wove through the tables in our direction. Desperately feigning nonrecognition, it was all I could do not to smile. To all appearances I was looking into my roommate's eyes. The next minute the girl was plopping her tray beside my roommate's, asking, "Is this seat taken?"

"It will be soon," I said.

Looking a bit disappointed, she asked my roommate, "By whom?"

"By *you!*" replied Kyle in a welcoming tone; then he laughed good-naturedly. She joined in the laughter and gracefully sat down, tossing her head, which sent her ponytail flying from side to side.

Turning toward me, my roommate said, "This is Christie-Anne, my lab partner in anatomy—"

Christie-Anne interrupted, "You don't have to introduce him—I recognize his voice. He's Mr. Stan, the voice on the radio program *Family Picnic,* who tells those adventurous stories about unbelievable miracles that occur in unexpected places all around the world."

"So you listen to the program." I twisted some spaghetti on my fork.

"I'm perhaps one of your biggest fans," Christie-Anne bubbled.

"Are you?" I said after chewing a mouthful of spaghetti.

"Perhaps I'm your only fan." She winked.

"Oh, really," I said. "I think radio personalities are the opposite of children—they're best heard, but not seen."

"I just love your stories—like the one where they tied up that prisoner in the cold and left him to die. Or the one with the boat ride with all the hippos in Africa. Wow!"

"Thank you." I felt the blood rush to my face, giving the appearance of an instant sunburn.

"I want you to write a story about me," Christie-Anne stated.

"Do you have a miraculous story to tell me?" I asked.

"Not yet," she confessed.

"I'm not going to write about you then, unless you tell me a miraculous story that I think is publishable," I said.

"Excuse me," Kyle blurted out suddenly, "I'm going for seconds." He pushed back his chair and strode toward the cafeteria line.

"He's quite a friendly guy, isn't he?" I commented after Kyle was beyond hearing range.

"Who?" asked Christie-Anne, "Ol' C-3PO?"*

"Is that what you call Kyle?" I made a mental note that Christie-Anne was most likely a serious *Star Wars* fan.†

"Guys who take nursing classes are, as far as we girls are concerned, either treated like one of us, or considered androids," she explained.

"You think my roommate's a droid?"‡

"He's so good with figures." Christie-Anne smiled. "I half expect him to predict the odds C-3PO-like by saying, 'The chances of you fainting while dissecting that frog are 9,102,583 to one!' " She laughed at her own joke. "No, but seriously, the girls want him for a lab partner because he knows all the formulas to solve the problems in chemistry and physics."

"So you like him?" I asked.

"I'd rather kiss a wookiee!"§ she shot back.

---

* C-3PO (/siːˈθriːpiːoʊ/) is a robot character from *Star Wars*. C-3PO is a protocol droid designed to serve human beings, and boasts that he is fluent in over six million forms of communication.

† For the record, this author, while studying at Andrews University, wrote a research paper on the religion and anthropology behind *Star Wars*.

‡ A kind of robot found in *Star Wars* like C-3PO.

§ Wookiees are a fictional species of hairy doglike bipeds in the *Star Wars* universe. Adult wookiees are typically taller than most humans, averaging 2.1 meters (6'11"). They possess enormous strength; wookiees have a keen sense of smell, are fully covered with a thick coat of hair. They also possess retractable claws, the better to aid them in climbing the great trees. Their leaping and movement ability is comparable to that of many tree-dwelling primates. Wookiees are devoted, loyal friends and are very distrustful of strangers.

Miracles in Unexpected Places!

"That can be arranged, Princess Leia,"* I replied playfully.

"I want you to be my Han Solo† and take me off on some adventure so you can write about me." Christie-Anne's comment surprised me.

"If you don't have an exciting story you want to tell me, I doubt I'm gonna write about you," I reminded her.

"Why not?"

" 'Cause in my experience, miraculous stories don't happen every day. Besides, my life's quite boring when I compare it to the stories I write."

"Boring," Christie-Anne rolled her eyes and said the word in a sing-song voice. "Humor me," she turned on a persuasive tone. "Why don't you tell me some place you haven't been?"

"Antarctica, Greenland, the North Pole, Eastern Europe—"

"See what I mean!" she exclaimed.

"I've been around the world at least nine times," I admitted. "So it's probably easier for me to tell you where I haven't been."

"My point exactly! You're like Han Solo and his hairy sidekick Chewbacca," Christie-Anne purred. "If I hang around you, I'm sure we'll have an adventure that you can write about."

"Nothing exciting enough to write about happens to me," I explained.

"You've gone to all those places, and you don't have any miraculous stories to tell?" she asked.

"Well, I've had my share of adventures," I reluctantly replied.

"Like?" She smiled, leaned forward, and gazed into my eyes.

Weakening under the pressure of her fawning eyes, I said, "I've swum with sharks in the Galapagos, swum through a whirlpool in the Gulf of Mexico, fought the receding tide in Puerto Rico, gotten robbed in an Italian train, and I almost forgot, gotten falsely arrested in Shanghai."

"You survived all that! Why don't you write about those stories?" Christie-Anne asked. "Whirlpools, sharks, and being shanghaied all sound like stories to me."

---

* Princess Leia Organa is characterized as a driven, dedicated woman with a forceful personality. The "petite, fair-skinned human female" is known perhaps as the most beautiful and remembered woman in the *Star Wars* universe.

† Han Solo is a reckless smuggler with a sarcastic wit; he is a very practical guy and considers himself a materialist; but the adventures in the first *Star Wars* movie evoke his compassion, a trait he didn't know he possessed.

Miracles in Unexpected Places

"Stories need a beginning, a middle, and an end along with conflict and drama. There's not much to write about in my whirlpool story. It's too simple—although I did pray and then swim out of it with difficulty."

"Tell me more," Christie-Anne enthused. "I'm all ears—they're floppy like a bunny rabbit, but all yours. What happened?"

"I was swimming in the Florida gulf and I saw a lot of horseshoe crabs on the beach and headed toward them. Suddenly I felt like I was being flushed down the toilet as the water whirled around me. After going under two or three times, I prayed. Then, with adrenaline rushing through me—and a tremendous will to live—I kicked extra hard and felt myself emerge on the other side of that swirling seawater. An old-timer sitting on the beach said, 'I saw you go under, lad. I thought you were a goner.' "

"Wow!" exclaimed Christie-Anne. "But you weren't a goner. You're sitting here telling me a pretty thrilling story that you don't think is worthy of a write-up. What a pity," she shook her head and clucked her tongue.

"Yeah," I shrugged. "It's a miracle I survived that whirlpool, but the story takes only a paragraph to tell, so, in my opinion, it's probably worth a footnote in someone's biography."

"Not to change the subject—"

"But you're about to," I interrupted.

"You're smarter than you look," she paused, then laughed when she saw my sad eyes. "Just joking! Oh, lighten up!" She smiled until I returned one, then continued, "Um, do you want me to answer the question you haven't asked me, but you wish you had?"

"I'm confused," I stammered. "Are you going to give me the question or the answer?"

"Here's the answer," Christie-Anne began. "Remember that I told you that girls in the nursing program like ol' C-3PO to be their lab partner because he's very good at helping us slice up a cat or come up with the algebraic formula for a chemistry experiment?"

"Yeah, where are we going with this?"

"Well, girls sit across from you at the cafeteria table, Mr. Stan, because, like Han Solo, you've got a bucket of bolts like the *Millennium Falcon** that can

---

* The *Millennium Falcon* is a spacecraft serving as a modified light freighter in the fictional *Star Wars* universe commanded by smuggler Han Solo and his wookiee first mate, Chewbacca.

speed a girl to a restaurant on a Saturday night at the speed of light, or at twelve parsecs,* whichever comes first."

"Did you just ask me out on a date this Saturday evening?"

"You're quicker than I thought!" Christie-Anne teased.

"What do you think?" I returned, not wanting to miss a beat. "Say, as quick as twelve parsecs?"

She laughed until she was gasping. "Be at the girls' dorm at eight—and don't be late. I'll let you select the restaurant we'll eat at."

"Well, if I'm going to be Han Solo," I said, "I'll need to have a wookiee as a copilot."

"Who's your wookiee?"

"My roommate."

"Why would you need ol' C-3PO?"

"My roommate may be a droid to you, but I need Chewbacca as copilot because he's got an uncanny sense of direction. Even when we leave the constellations out of the picture, he's got a nose for north!"

"Well," Christie-Anne smiled, "why don't you ask him yourself."

"I'll have to ask him about his schedule later," I said, trying to buy some time before committing, "when he comes."

"I see your wookiee heading this way with a tray of food to wolf down. You'll soon have your opportunity to arrange for your copilot."

I gulped, feeling awkward because Christie-Anne was my roommate's lab partner and she'd asked me out.

When Kyle joined us again, he asked, "Did I miss anything?"

"We were talking about what to do this Saturday night," I began tentatively, then thought to myself, I guess my rickety old jalopy was the way to begin. "Would you like to ride with us to a restaurant?"

"Who's us?" Kyle said suspiciously.

"Mr. Stan and I," Christie-Anne twisted her hair with a finger and cocked her head to the side as she smiled sweetly at Kyle.

"I'd love it if you came," I hastily added.

Kyle's eyes had melted into puppy-dog eyes as he looked at Christie-Anne's smile. It's obvious he'd do anything for her. "You two go ahead."

---

* The parsec (symbol: pc) is a unit of length used in astronomy, equal to about 30.9 trillion kilometers (19.2 trillion miles) or 3.26 light-years.

"Seriously," I said in disbelief. "It's Saturday night—time to unwind."

"I can't go this time," he said sheepishly. "I've got an auditing project due Monday, so I've got to study this weekend. Let me take a rain check on that."

"Rain check in the middle of winter," I said. "There's a foot of snow out there, and you want to wait for the rain?"

"You know what I mean." Kyle smiled.

"If you say so," my voice clearly sounded resigned. "I'll be glad to chaperone you two in a week or so." I'd really have preferred to have Kyle along at the meal. I was not feeling comfortable with Christie-Anne's *Star Wars* analogy of me being Han Solo to her Princess Leia. I thought it'd be better if Kyle was the proverbial Han and I, Luke Skywalker.* Looking at Kyle, though, it wasn't that easy, as he was the height of a wookiee and, well, truth be told, I was too tall to be Luke. Besides, unlike Luke, I was no farm boy. Poor Kyle, I lamented. If I could be Leia's Luke, we'd end up brother and sister, and then I wouldn't feel like my roommate and I were competing for the same girl. Why had Christie-Anne placed me—us—in this situation? I wondered.

Christie-Anne picked up her tray to leave, "I'll see you at the dorm at eight—and don't be late, Mr. Stan. Unlike most girls, it won't take me long to get ready."

"I'll keep that in mind." I followed Kyle out of the cafeteria.

* * * * *

Saturday night I picked up Christie-Anne at eight and we drove off toward the restaurant. The temperature had dropped earlier in the day making the icy winter road slick and demanding caution at the wheel. I began to relax when I saw that the two-lane highway appeared to clear. Suddenly I realized it wasn't pavement, "Black ice!" I exclaimed to Christie-Anne.

I gripped the wheel as I felt the car slip. With a car speeding toward me in the other lane, I knew if I stepped on the brake I'd skid directly into it. I had but a split second to choose between landing in a snowbank or hitting a car. Instantly I steered away from the oncoming car and veered off the side of the road, coming to an abrupt stop in a three-foot snowbank. I tried to open the door but it was stuck. Christie-Anne's door didn't open either.

---

* Luke Skywalker is the main protagonist of the original film trilogy of *Star Wars*.

Miracles in Unexpected Places!

"That was a miracle!" Christie-Anne claimed. "You'll have to write about this," she added.

"Write about this, I won't. Miracle it was not," I contended in my best Yoda* imitation. "In control, I was."

"No you weren't. Look! We're in a snowbank. And hey, you can't be Yoda," Christie-Anne said. "You're my Han Solo. You should be shouting, 'It's not my fault!' "—a line Han Solo oft claimed whenever his spaceship failed to reach light speed.

"Hmm, before too late it was, turn the wheel, I did, hmm. Into the snowbank, we plunged," I replied, preferring to be Yoda in this scenario because it gave my roommate another chance with his lab partner. "Getting stuck in a snowbank is a miracle, you think, hmm?" I asked.

"It was!" she enthused. "We almost hit that oncoming car, but at the last minute your guardian angel turned the wheel into the snowbank and saved our lives."

"Had something to do with it, an angel most likely did not," I protested. "My choice, it was. While still in control, I was, steering wheel toward snowbank, I turned. Hitting car head on, I presume you preferred. That choice, I would not make. Our lives, I must save. Good choice, hmm! Good choice, you think I make, hmm, hmm?"

"Stop it with the Yoda voice!" she said as she laughed, then turning serious, she looked me in the eye. "Did you see the expression on the face of the driver we almost hit?"

"No, driving on ice, I was." I put up my hand before she could protest my use of Yoda's inverted diction.

"I'm sure he expected we'd collide," she asserted.

"We wouldn't have crashed," I protested, dropping the Yoda impersonation. "I had the situation in control."

There was a knocking on the window. We looked in the direction of the sound. "It's the driver you almost hit," Christie-Anne said.

I rolled the window down.

"That was pretty amazing," the young man said as he reached out his hand.

---

* Yoda is a powerful Jedi Master in the *Star Wars* universe. Yoda's race and home world have not been named in any media, canonical or otherwise, and he is merely said to be of a "species unknown." Yoda's speech syntax has been analyzed and discussed by academic syntacticians, who found it somewhat inconsistent, but could extrapolate that "Yodic" has object-subject-verb word order.

Miracles in Unexpected Places

We shook hands through the window. "I saw you coming 'round that corner and was certain we'd crash and I held my breath. The next thing I knew, you were in a snowbank."

"I'm used to riding on ice and I knew the only thing I could do was turn. It was either turn into you or into the snowbank," I said.

"Yeah," said the driver, "I saw you turn the steering wheel to the right."

"And then we landed here!" I finished.

"Right," he confirmed. "You're in pretty deep. It looks like you really can't dig your way out of this snow. It's too deep."

"That's for sure," I replied. "We can't even open the doors."

"Do you have a phone along?" he asked.

I told him we didn't bring our phones.

"Would you like me to call a tow truck?"

"That'd be great!" Christie-Anne said. "We gotta get home soon."

"I'll do that," he said. "One should be coming along in about an hour or so. Just wanted you to know I decided it was only right for me to stop and help you. Your quick thinking may have saved my life tonight. I'm glad we met the way we did instead of head-on."

"That makes three of us," I said and we all laughed nervously. The driver turned to go, leaving us to await the tow truck.

"Well, here we are. So much for speeding in your *Millennium Falcon* at twelve parsecs to that Saturday night restaurant," Christie-Anne lamented as she leaned against the passenger door and grinned impishly.

Time seemed to tick slowly. "I wish I could use the force* like Obi-Wan Kenobi and with a wave of a hand lift this car out of this snowbank and be on our merry way to the restaurant," I said.

Christie-Anne laughed, "I tried to use the force on my parents, thinking they were the simple minded."[†] She waved her hand in the air. " 'You're not going to give me broccoli and carrots for lunch. You're going to give me cookies

---

* In the original *Star War's* film, the Force is first described as an energy field created by all living things, that surrounds and penetrates living beings and binds the galaxy together. The idea of the force is: "Many people feel that in the contemplation of nature and in communication with other living things, they become aware of some kind of force, or something, behind this apparent mask which we see in front of us, and they call it God." The use of the force often appears incredible or miraculous.

† There are those, like Obi-Wan Kenobi, who know how to use the Force for good, and then there are *the simple minded,* who are susceptible to it, while others resist it, calling it simple mind tricks.

and ice cream.' It never worked. I still had to eat my vegetables. So I guess we're at the mercy of the tow truck whenever it comes."

"I suppose the police will discover us sooner or later if that driver didn't follow up on his promise," I said.

"Mr. Stan, remember, when Han said, 'May the force be with you,' his voice sounded like he wasn't quite convinced. It was a superstition. Like Han, Mr. Stan, you're no Jedi.* When it comes to the force, you're a bit of an agnostic." Christie-Anne waxed elegant. "To put it bluntly, you wouldn't know a miracle if it hit you between the eyes."

"When Luke made that one-in-a-million bull's eye shot that blew up the Death Star,† Han seemed to respect the force," I replied. "I do see miracles around me. That's why I write about them. However, I believe there's a perfectly logical explanation for what happened tonight." I turned the radio to golden oldies. After listening awhile, I suggested, "Let's parody the songs to fit our own lives. You need to sing with the artist and make it rhyme, are you game?"

"Anything you can do I can do better," Christie-Anne boasted.

"We'll see," I countered as a new song began to air. "Oh, that's a Billy Joel‡ song!" I exclaimed. "I love the chorus. I think the song's called 'Lunatic.' "

"You May Be Right," Christie-Anne retorted.

"I just might be." I replied, pleased, but clueless.

"No, wise guy, that's the name of the song—'You May Be Right.' "

"Funny," I wrinkled my face. "I guess that means you know this song too." She nodded. "Then let's sing the chorus together." We sang about how I could be crazy and that I could be the lunatic she's lookin' for. "Now I'll parody a stanza," I said.

---

* The Jedi /ˈdʒɛˌdaɪ/ are a monastic organization in the *Star Wars* universe. They study, serve, and use a mystical power called the Force. As guardians of peace and justice in the galaxy, they mediate peace negotiations among planets and other factions and, if necessary, use their formidable fighting skills, agility and wisdom to quickly end unrest or neutralize dangerous individuals or threats. The Jedi are governed by a council, consisting of twelve of the most powerful and wise members of the Jedi Order. They are bound to a code of ethics, morality, principles, and justice. The Jedi are trained to use the Force through passive meditation, practicing selflessness, and commitment to justice while at the same time rejecting emotions such as passion, fear, anger, and hate.

† A Death Star is a fictional moon-sized space station and superweapon appearing in the *Star Wars* movies.

‡ William Martin "Billy" Joel is an American pianist, singer-songwriter, and composer.

"I saw you sitting over there
in the Chevrolet's passenger's chair.
I made you groan at puns until you smiled.
You went out with a man
and took me as I am
'cause you enjoyed to have some madness for awhile. . . .
I drove the Chevy on the ice,
and when it skid, did not think twice.
I turned the wheel toward a pile of snow.
You feared you'd not survive,
but we'll make it home alive.
And so you thought that meant we should be towed."

We laughed as we sang the chorus about my being a lunatic again.

Suddenly a pair of bright lights blinded us. A driver jumped from a pickup, approached the window, and motioned for me to roll it down. "Someone called saying you needed a tow," he drawled. "Yeah, you look pretty stuck. I won't ask what happened. Can you get out?" We shook our heads. "I'll pull you guys to the road, then lower the car so you can get out and jump into my truck. I'll take you down to the station where we can take care of this bill and you'll be on your way." The driver headed for his tow truck, backed toward the car, and hooked a chain to the axle. Soon Christie-Anne and I were sitting next to the driver as he sped down the highway toward town with the Chevy in tow.

Once at the station, I paid the bill, and we headed back to the dorm where I dropped Christie-Anne off after saying good night and apologizing for letting her go to bed hungry.

She said, "You were quite the bard, singing tonight's little adventure into legend."

"That I did," I said.

"You might want to write up the lyrics," she coaxed.

I allowed that I'd think about it, and we said our goodbyes. Soon I was under the covers of my bed in my warm dorm room and fast asleep.

* * * * *

Miracles in Unexpected Places!

The next day commenced like any other day until I stood in the cafeteria with my tray in hand looking for an empty table. Was it my imagination, or was most everyone looking at me? Becoming self-conscious, I wanted to reach my hand up my back to see if someone had taped a sign to it saying "Kick me!" or worse, but I didn't want to spill the food on my tray. A girl who'd read the perplexed look on my face approached and whispered as she passed, "Everybody's talking about your crazy night in the snowbank; then you walked in. That's why they're looking at you."

"You mean Christie-Anne's been telling everyone?" I asked, wondering what her version of the story was and suddenly losing my appetite.

"She may have told a friend or two," the girl replied. "A good story like that spreads."

"What's there to tell?" I asked. The girl smiled knowingly, deposited her tray on the rack and left.

Nonplussed, I sat at an empty table and picked at my food.

Kyle soon joined me; we ate quietly. "You call me Chewy?" he broke the silence.

I nodded my head. How much of the story did Christie-Anne tell?

Kyle smiled, "I like it," he said to my surprise. "Chewbacca is my favorite *Star Wars* character. I guess I do sorta resemble him, and he generally does get the last word. You can call me Chewy!"

"I think it's better than C-3PO," I stuffed a slice of pizza in my mouth.

"Is that what she calls me?" When I nodded again, Kyle tried to move his hands metallically. The absurdity of it made us both laugh.

Just then Christie-Anne, wearing one humungous smile, stood across from me, holding her tray. "And where's that lunatic I think I'm looking for?" Her eyes twinkled as she sat down.

"Do you mean Billy Joel?" I teased. "Last I heard, he's married to an uptown girl."*

"What!" Christie-Anne feigned disgust. "Are you ashamed of me just because I was born in an Appalachian shack like Dolly Parton?† I'll have you know I'm a Yankee New Englander from Maine—where the Appalachian Trail begins. And no, I'm not talking about that lunatic Billy Joel, I'm asking about that

---

* "Uptown Girl" is the title of a Billy Joel song about his wife, the supermodel Christie Brinkley.

† Dolly Rebecca Parton is an American singer-songwriter, multi-instrumentalist, actress, author, and philanthropist, best known for her work in country music.

insane driver who took me out on a date I'll never forget!"

"Guilty as charged!" I admitted, hanging my head in mock shame, but I couldn't resist grinning, which soon became contagious.

"I've never had anyone almost kill me on my first date," she smiled broadly.

"Almost kill you—phooey—I saved your life!" I defended myself.

"Is that your version of the story? I was there, too, you know," Christie-Anne rolled her eyes.

"You weren't in the driver's seat, so the experience wasn't identical," I replied. "Being in the passenger seat, you were in a different world. You weren't making the decisions."

"You forget that we both got towed Saturday night," Christie-Anne reminded me. "I can't imagine what you're going to do for an encore."

Slightly astonished, my eyes widened. "Does that mean you want me to drive you someplace this weekend?"

"After our first snow adventure, I'd be a fool not to," Christie-Anne answered. "I want to give you more stories to write about," she winked.

"I'll take that rain check this weekend," Kyle piped in. "I'd love you to chaperone us on another adventure like the last."

"Gladly!" I replied. "You're on! We'll be a friendly threesome, like the Musketeers,* though I don't make a habit of driving into snowbanks."

"Landing in that snowbank was truly a miracle," Christie-Anne asserted. "You're gonna have to write that up for your next episode of Mr. Stan on *Family Picnic.*"

Not again, I thought. "Christie-Anne, there's a perfectly good explanation for what happened that night," I sighed. "I turned the wheel just before the car lost control and we came to a stop in the snowbank."

"You're such a materialist," she clucked her tongue in protest. "I realize that scientists can explain all the elements that make life; however, they still can't replicate it themselves. None of them, by their own efforts, can make a rose open in the morning. Just because you can explain it doesn't mean it isn't a miracle," she asserted. "All I know is that I saw my life flash before my eyes when we landed in that snowbank. Sometimes, I'll admit, I'm a preacher's wayward daughter, but last night I felt God was close to us. I wanted to make sure I was

---

* Three legendary swordsmen—Athos, Porthos, and Aramis—at the court of Louis XIII in seventeenth-century France.

Miracles in Unexpected Places!

His child. When I got home that night, I prayed to renew that relationship. I'm a better Christian now thanks to last night's episode."

What could I say to that? Nothing really, so I didn't. Actually, I couldn't have said it better myself.

The three of us then made arrangements to eat at the restaurant Christie-Anne and I had been unable to eat at the night before. It felt good to chaperone my roommate. Then we went our separate ways.

Back in my dorm room, I jotted down some notes about that snowbank on scrap paper, then crumpled them up, and tossed them on the floor. Later that night I sat staring at a blank computer screen, ready to write the next story for *Family Picnic*. What story should I tell? In my writing of miracle stories, did Christie-Anne have a point? When I choose to write about the most dramatic and undeniable miracles, do I miss the simple ones that occur daily? Certainly God gave me the wisdom to make that split second decision that got us towed from the snow. That whole thought process was a miracle of biochemical interactions and synapses along a line of neurons.

While I cannot truly say that the accident in the snow was a miracle, it was clear that it did build faith in Christie-Anne's heart. Isn't a miracle something that builds faith in the mind of the observer? I knew the answer to that question was a resounding Yes. I picked up the crumpled pieces of paper I'd scribbled on earlier, flattened them out on the corner of the desk, and reread them. They had potential. Indeed, I reasoned, Christie-Anne would be happy to hear that I'd written a miracle story about her! Without looking at the keyboard or the screen, I typed four words and stared at the computer screen again. I'd just typed a working title for the next story—one that I'd repeatedly said I'd never write: *Miracles in Unexpected Places.*

Chapter 18

For a Shilling and Sixpence

Here is a wonderful little story about a certain missionary in Africa. I'm sure you'll love it as much as I did when I first heard it told by my father back when I was just a little boy of ten. The story shows how God works to help us when we are in danger. I don't know what the missionary's name was or where exactly he worked in former British East Africa, but I do know that his story is as true as it is delightful.

The missionary in our story urgently needed to transport some medicine to a certain doctor so that he could treat some of his patients. He had been asked to take the medicine to a caravan of trucks—locally called lorries—before morning, or the medicine would never reach the doctor on time. The lorry drivers would carry the medicine the rest of the way to the doctor. To get to the trucks, the missionary needed to travel by boat down the Zambezi River.

So he went down to the riverbank to find some boatmen to row him down the river to his agreed point of rendezvous with the trucks. After haggling over the price with several boatmen, he eventually settled on a crew who agreed to take him for three ha'pence (which at that time in British East Africa was a satisfactory wage.)

He followed them down to their wooden canoe. A couple of the oarsmen walked to the front of their narrow dugout and sat down. With medicine in hand, the missionary followed. Trying to balance his steps on the wobbly canoe, he sat in the middle and tied down the medicine. Two other rowers sat in back.

For a Shilling and Sixpence

The crew leader kicked off and stepped aboard. As they paddled along, they sang a slow rhythmic song that went something like this: *"Hooss! Hooss! Hooss!"* Each *"hooss"* helped them coordinate their strokes as they headed downstream. The song, the strokes, and the gentle swaying of the canoe slowly lulled the missionary into a dreamy state.

Suddenly, the boat went *bump* against the riverbank. The oarsmen arose, walked on the rim of the canoe and jumped ashore, leaving the poor missionary sitting in the boat, bewildered. He called after them, saying, "Why have we stopped? We haven't reached our destination. I must reach the trucks tonight. People's lives are at stake!"

The crew leader shook his head and said, "No, *bwana,* not tonight. We take you first thing in the morning."

Leaving the medicine on the boat, the missionary came ashore and pleaded with the boatmen. "But it's not dark yet. If we go in the morning, I'll miss the trucks, and the people won't be able to get their medicine. We struck a deal."

The leader smiled broadly. "I know, bwana. We take you down river, don't worry, bwana. First thing in the morning."

"When we started out on this trip, I told you I had to reach my destination tonight." The missionary spoke patiently, "Tomorrow is too late. Why can't we go tonight?"

"So sorry, bwana. When we make agreement, we think we be able to row faster and get where you want sooner. We failed. So sorry, bwana. We know this river well. After dark, hippos come out and fill river. They could kill us." The missionary thought he saw a shiver go up and down the leader's spine. "No, bwana, no!" The leader shook his head. "Please, we cannot go tonight. First thing in the morning, bwana. First thing in the morning!"

The missionary smiled. "If it's only hippos that worry you, then there's no problem. Let's go. I'm not afraid of hippos."

"You should be, bwana. If we make a hippo angry, it could open its big mouth and cut our small canoe in half. Then we drown and no one gets medicine!"

"There's no need to fear," the missionary urged. "Listen, my guardian angel will protect us from the hippos. I believe God wants me to help save lives." He reached out his hand and placed it on the crew leader's shoulder. "Let's go now. We must meet that truck caravan tonight."

"First thing in the morning, bwana!" the leader replied.

Desperate, the missionary thought of another solution. "Would you take me down tonight if I were to offer you sixpence?"

The eyes of the leader grew as big as saucers. Excusing himself, he met with his crew. They huddled tightly together, discussing the offer. "What do you think?" he asked the others.

"I'm not going tonight," whined one rower. "Think of all those terrible hippos!"

"Yeah, I agree," grumbled another. "We could lose our boat—or even get killed. Think of our families."

"But he just offered us sixpence. That's half a shilling," said a third. "That's a lot of money. Think of what we could do for our families with that money!" There were murmurs of assent.

The leader smiled, revealing some missing teeth. "Are we agreed then?" They took a vote. Hippos were forgotten.

Breaking from their huddle, the leader returned to where the missionary stood, awaiting their decision. "Shall we go now?" the missionary asked.

"For your offer of sixpence—half a shilling—we think we can make it, bwana. For half a shilling!" They climbed back into the dugout, resumed their former seating arrangement, and shoved off.

Soon the rowers started the song that helped them row in rhythm. *"Hooss! Hooss! Hooss!"* The missionary noticed that it was being sung an octave higher and that the rhythm was twice as fast. The boat sped downstream at twice the speed it had before. Before long, dusk fell over the river, and then ripples of moonlight on the water guided the oarsmen downstream.

Suddenly, in the darkness, they heard a loud "grunt"! There was a great big hippo to the right of the boat. Then they heard another loud "grunt"! There was a great big hippo to the left of the boat. Soon they heard a third "grunt." There was a great big hippo right behind the boat. The missionary mused to himself: *Suppose there is a hippo right in front of the boat?*

Suddenly, the boat went, *bump!*

The missionary looked ahead, straining in the darkness to see if they'd hit a hippo. Then he realized that the boat had been docked. The crew jumped out and huddled on the riverbank.

Without getting out, the missionary asked, "What's wrong? We aren't there yet. Take me downriver. We have miles to go. Time is running out. If we don't hurry, we'll miss those trucks!"

For a Shilling and Sixpence

The crew leader shook his head, and the missionary thought he saw another shiver run up and down the boatman's body. "First thing in the morning!" The leader's voice shuddered. "We cannot go any further tonight, bwana. First thing in the morning."

Disappointed, the missionary said, "We had a deal. For half a shilling you promised to help me meet all the trucks so I can save lives with medicine."

"Please, bwana. We must not go any further," the rowers insisted. "Please, let's stop here. We take you first thing in the morning!"

The missionary stepped off the boat. "Men," he urged. "After coming this far, we can't stop now. We must finish the trip."

"No, bwana." The rowers shook their heads.

The leader added, "We know the Zambezi better than you, bwana. Up ahead are twice as many hippos as there were behind us. We cannot go on tonight. It's too dangerous. First thing in the morning. We'll be safe from hippos. Please, bwana, first thing in the morning."

"Don't worry about the hippos, men," the missionary said. "I told you that my guardian angel will protect us all the way because we are on an important mission for God."

The rowers shuffled their feet.

"Let's get back in the boat and row on. We're losing precious time!" The missionary turned to board the boat, then stopped in his tracks when he heard the leader say, "Please, bwana, first thing in the morning."

Approaching the leader, the missionary said, "If you don't trust my guardian angel, could you take me down tonight if I gave you a shilling?"

The eyes of the leader grew big—bigger than they had earlier when he'd been offered half a shilling. He huddled again with his men. "What do you say?" he asked.

"I don't want to die," whined the first rower. "I'm afraid of those hippos' mouths. I've seen what they can do to a little boat like ours. First thing in the morning!"

"There are twice as many hippos ahead," grumbled the second oarsman. "What if they snap our boat in two with their powerful jaws? We'd be out of business! Then how would we support our families? No, I won't go tonight."

Then another rower spoke up. "But he offered us a whole shilling. That's easily more than fifteen times our regular fare!"

Miracles in Unexpected Places

The leader looked at the others. "A shilling is indeed a lot of money. Are we agreed?" They voted a second time and once again the hippos, with their mighty jaws, were forgotten. The leader returned to the missionary. "We know that there are twice as many hippos ahead, bwana, but for a shilling, we think we can take you tonight. For a shilling we'll climb back into the boat and row!"

They returned to their places in the canoe. The missionary was once again sitting in the middle. Two rowers were in front and three sat in back. After the kickoff, the oarsmen sang a little song as they rowed. This time, when they sang it, the missionary noted that it was sung even faster than the second time. They seemed to clip off the *s* sound in their *"hoosses"* as they sped downstream. Their song sounded more like, *"Who! Who! Who!"*

Then out of the darkness the missionary heard, *Grunt! Grunt!* There were two great big hippos to the right of the boat.

Grunt! Grunt! There were two large hippos to the left of the boat.

Grunt! Grunt! There were two huge hippos right behind the boat. The missionary wondered what would happen if there were two great big hippos right in front of the boat! Suddenly, the boat went *bump* against the shore.

Immediately, the crew hurried out of the boat, leaving the poor missionary sitting in the middle. He begged them to get back in the boat and continue the trip, but they were stubborn. "Please, bwana," the leader entreated, "we take you first thing in the morning. Too dangerous to go farther tonight. Up ahead there are twice as many hippos as there were behind. We won't make it tonight. First thing in the morning, bwana! Please, first thing in the morning. Not tonight!"

The missionary came ashore. "Remember what I said about my angel? You have no need to fear. Let's get back in the boat and proceed. I need to catch those trucks tonight. People's lives are at stake!"

The crew leader still refused. Then the missionary said, "Would you take me tonight for a shilling *and* sixpence?"

The crew leader's mouth dropped open and his eyes grew as big as cooking pots. In minutes he was huddled with his men. Some of them grumbled about the hippos again, but then they agreed. Returning to the missionary, they replied, "Please, bwana, for a shilling *and* sixpence—nobody has ever paid us that much for this trip before! For a shilling *and* sixpence, we think we can take you tonight."

For a Shilling and Sixpence

So, after everybody returned to their places in the boat, the leader pushed off again. As they rode down the dark river, the men sang a song to synchronize their paddling. The song sounded more like a hissing snake. *"Hiss! Hiss! Hiss!"* they sang. In the moonlight, the missionary thought he could see the neck of the boatman immediately in front of him. The tiny hairs on the back of his neck seemed to straighten up and stand on end!

Then in the darkness he heard, *Grunt! Grunt! Grunt! Grunt!* Four great big hippos to the left of the boat!

Grunt! Grunt! Grunt! Grunt! Four large hippos to the right of the boat!

Grunt! Grunt! Grunt! Grunt! Four huge hippos right behind the boat! *What if there are four hippos right in front of the boat?* Before the missionary could ponder the question in depth, the boat went *bump* against the shore.

In the distance he could hear engines warming up. He saw the line of trucks he was supposed to catch preparing to depart. The rowers leaped ashore. The missionary wasn't far behind.

Before heading to the trucks, the missionary took out a shilling and sixpence and offered them to the crew leader. He refused it. Puzzled, the missionary offered it to the next oarsmen, but he shook his head. He tried to give the coins to the other boatmen, but they all refused. "Come on," he urged. "Take it. It's yours. You've earned it!" None of them moved.

One by one, they all shook their heads. "Please, bwana, you keep it," they insisted. Then the leader spoke up. "As we rowed in the dark, we watched your guardian angel pushing hippos this way and that way so we could paddle safely between them. After seeing your angel at work tonight, bwana, no, we cannot accept your money!"

The missionary was amazed. He'd seen no angel that night. Surely, the angel's brightness must have made quite a contrast in the dark of night. Perhaps the light had guided them. He smiled to himself as he imagined his angel shoving the clumsy beasts aside or piling them atop each other to make a path for the little boat. Instantly, he thanked God for revealing his angel to the crew. Pocketing the coins, he bid the rowers farewell, approached the trucks, and delivered the medicine.

And it arrived at its destination on time.

Chapter 19

Badfish and Big Brother

Dr. C. Mervyn Maxwell sat next to his five-year-old son, Stanley.* Stanley had just been tucked into bed, and he was anxiously waiting for his father to tell him a story.

"So, would you like an early church-history story, would you like an Adventist Church story, would you like an animal story, or—"

"Daddy, you always tell me *true* stories," Stanley interrupted.

"Don't you like true stories?" Dr. Maxwell asked.

"Oh, yes, Daddy," Stanley said. "I love your stories. It's just—well—er—could you tell me a made-up story for once? Just tell me one this one time, and I'll never ask you again. Please, Daddy?"

Dr. Maxwell thought for a moment, a story beginning to form in his head of a conflict between two fish. "All right," Daddy said. He paused again, giving himself a few seconds to outline the plot. Then he began the story.

"Two young damselfish swam out of the reef. Now, these fish knew very well that they were disobeying the rules when they swam from the reef, for they might be eaten by Badfish the Barracuda." Dr. Maxwell said the name with great emphasis, extending the *dah* sound after Barracuda for several seconds. "As the two fish began to nibble on the algae that they had swum out

---

* Once again, the Stanley in this story is Stanley M. Maxwell. This story was written by the author's daughter, Roxy Maxwell, and edited by the author. It is her version of how she remembers the author telling this story to her.

to eat, they didn't notice the large fish swimming closer and closer. Then one of them looked up and shouted for all he was worth, 'Look out! It's Badfish! Badfish! Badfish is coming!' The two fish immediately turned on their tail fins and flapped their fins as fast as they could. They made it back just in the nick of time, causing Badfish to bump his nose against the reef, the smell of his own blood driving him crazy."

Dr. Maxwell lowered his voice, and, pretending to be Badfish, he said, " 'You got away this time!' Badfish shouted angrily, 'but next time . . .' " Dr. Maxwell suddenly burst out his best evil laugh. " '*Yeehahaha!* Next time—there will be no next time! Then you'll be fin of my fin and scale of my scale!' And with that, Badfish swam away.

"The older fish in the reef often talked of the prophecy that told of Big Brother, a porcupine fish that would one day be born to the reef. Big Brother would kill Badfish and free the reef fish from the fear of being eaten by Badfish. Then the fish would be able to swim in and out of the reef, with no more worries of being eaten by Badfish.

"One day," Dr. Maxwell continued, "the oldest fish in the reef witnessed something he'd never seen before in all his years. He was watching the baby fish hatching, but one particular egg caught his eye. It was different from all the other fish. It had sort of a very light yellow tint to it, and when the other fish swam over to it, it puffed up like a balloon with spikes. Then the oldest fish in the reef knew that this was a porcupine fish, perhaps even the one in the prophecy.

"The porcupine fish grew and attended the school of fish like all other little fishes, and there he learned about the rule never to swim outside of the reef, and of the prophecy of Big Brother. As he heard of the prophecy, the porcupine fish thought, *Big Brother is a porcupine fish; I am a porcupine fish; maybe . . .*

"Some time later, as the porcupine fish was swimming along the edge of the reef—still following the rules—Badfish the Barracuda swam up to him." Dr. Maxwell lowered his voice again, and with a fierce look on his face that made Stanley squirm under his covers, he spoke as if he were Badfish, " 'Come out, and I'll eat you up!' Badfish flashed porcupine fish a huge, toothy grin." And so did Dr. Maxwell.

" 'Oh, no, you wouldn't want to eat me right now,' the porcupine fish said.

" 'And why not?' Badfish boomed grouchily. 'I'm hungry, and there aren't any fish outside of the reef right now.'

" 'Because I'm too small,' the porcupine fish replied.

" 'What?'

" 'Badfish,' the porcupine fish said earnestly. 'Right now I'm so small I would be no more than a grain of sand in your teeth. Wait until I'm bigger, and then I'll let you eat me, and I'll fill your belly so full you won't have to eat for a long time.'

"Badfish pondered this for a minute, and then thought that this porcupine fish indeed had a good point. 'You're right,' Badfish said. 'You are too small. I'm not going to eat you today. Instead, I'll wait 'til you're bigger before I gobble you up. But you must keep your side of the promise. You must come out so I can eat you.'

" 'Oh, I'll come out, Badfish. When I'm bigger, I will. I promise.'

" 'Well, that's one deal I'll definitely keep!' Badfish laughed evilly and then swam away. The porcupine fish, eager to get away from the encounter, quickly swam farther back into the reef.

"Time passed. The porcupine fish grew bigger and bigger, eating more than most of the fish ate, preparing for the day when he would meet Badfish. But eating wasn't the only way he prepared. Every once in a while he'd swim over to one of his friends and say, 'Bet you can't scare me.' So then the other fish would make himself look as scary as he could." Dr. Maxwell made a hideous-looking face and kept it up as he continued. "And he'd swim toward the porcupine fish and go, 'Boo!' "

"Daddy, fish don't say 'Boo!' " Stanley interrupted.

"OK, then let's say his friend made the fishy equivalent of 'Boo!' " Dr. Maxwell quickly amended the story, and this correction satisfied his son. "So, the fish would swim up to porcupine fish with that scary look on his face and try to scare him, and more often than not, he wouldn't be able to."

"Why not?" Stanley asked curiously.

"Because you see, son, the porcupine fish was trying to make it so he wouldn't get scared too easily, and then he wouldn't puff up when he saw Badfish, and then Badfish would be able to eat him more easily."

"Oh," Stanley said. "Go on with the story, Daddy, go on!"

"The porcupine fish grew bigger and bigger. Soon he felt he was big enough to meet Badfish.

"So he swam over to the edge of the reef and called, 'Badfish! I'm ready for you!'

"Badfish, hearing his name, swam over toward the sound. As soon as Badfish saw the porcupine fish, he smiled broadly, showing all of his shiny, knifelike teeth. 'Who dared call my name?'

" 'It is I,' the porcupine fish said, 'Notice anything different?'

" 'No, just another reef fish,' Badfish said. 'What am I supposed to see?'

" 'I'm bigger!'

" 'Ah yes.' He grinned broadly. 'Indeed you have grown bigger. Now you're more than just a grain of sand in my teeth. Soon you'll be fin of my fin and scale of my scale. Come out now, as you promised. You know I can't eat you from in there.'

"So the porcupine fish swam out of the reef. Badfish opened his mouth wide, and, after porcupine fish swam willingly into Badfish's mouth, Badfish swallowed the porcupine fish in one gulp.

"The porcupine fish stayed inside Badfish's belly for some time, and then, when he felt the time was right, he began puffing himself up. And he puffed, and he puffed, and he puffed. Bigger and bigger he got until one of his spines poked a hole in Badfish's belly." Dr. Maxwell poked his finger into Stanley's belly, causing the boy to squirm excitedly for a few seconds. "As soon as one of his spines had poked a hole," Dr. Maxwell continued, "the porcupine fish began to nibble at the edge of the hole, slowly chewing it bigger.

"Meanwhile, Badfish was feeling as if he had bit off a little more than he could chew, for he now had the most terrible bellyache he'd ever had. Swimming around madly, he desperately tried in vain to get rid of his stomachache. And as the porcupine fish was nibbling on the hole, gradually making it wider and wider, Badfish swam more and more wildly." This entire time, whenever Dr. Maxwell told of Badfish's swimming around wildly, he would wave his hand back and forth in a rapid motion, and when he told of the porcupine fish's nibbling on the hole in Badfish's side, he would put his thumb and index finger together, pinching them.

"Finally," Dr. Maxwell continued, "the hole was big enough for the porcupine fish to swim out. As soon as he'd swum out, Badfish sank slowly to the bottom of the seafloor and was no more. The porcupine fish then swam back to the reef and told the reef fish that Badfish was dead, and that they no longer needed to fear being eaten by Badfish. All the fish in the reef cheered! 'Hurrah!' Many of the fish shouted, 'Hurray for the porcupine fish! You're our Big Brother, for you have saved us from Badfish! Hurrah! Hurrah!'

"There was a great celebration in the reef that day. And during that celebration, the porcupine fish silently swam away to another reef. A few of the fish saw him go. Many of those fish who watched him leave saw just an ordinary puffer fish. But some of them saw him as Big Brother, the porcupine fish from the prophecy, who had saved them from the fear of being eaten by Badfish."

"That's a really good story," Stanley said.

"I'm glad you liked it. Now, can you tell me what it means?"

"Of course, Daddy. The porcupine fish is supposed to be Jesus, and Badfish is Satan."

"And what about the two fish in the beginning?" Daddy asked.

Stanley thought for a while, and then exclaimed triumphantly, "Adam and Eve!"

"Right. I knew you were a smart lad," Dr. Maxwell said, beaming at his son. He started to get up, and then with a twinkle in his eye, he said, "Now, it's time for all little boys under the age of ten to go to sleep."

"But I'm only five!" Stanley protested.

"Exactly. Good night, Stanley," Daddy said as he kissed his son on his forehead.

"Good night, Daddy."

* * * * *

Years later, when young Stanley was in college, he remembered this story and decided to do some research on it. There he found out that his father, who didn't know much about fish behavior when he'd devised this story, had made up an allegory that was actually scientifically accurate. Schools of fish really do live in reefs where, as long as they remain in the reef, they are safe from barracudas and some sharks. Also, porcupine fish really do puff up in the bellies of their consumers and have been known to eat their way out of a shark's stomach. Later, Stanley wrote up his own version of this story, adding all kinds of different fish species, putting even more great controversy details into it, but he never forgot the original story, the story that his father made up that one night when he, as a five-year-old boy, wanted to hear a made-up story just once. He told it to his daughter, Roxy, for the first time when she was five, and now she has written it up for you to enjoy, at whatever age you are.

Chapter 20

Nelly's Fright and Ellen G. White

It was 1868. Nelly was fourteen. A few years earlier she'd immigrated to America from England and settled with her mother near Battle Creek, Michigan. Nelly and her mother attended prayer meeting regularly on Friday evenings.

It was June 12. Brother James and Sister White had been away from Battle Creek, and they had just returned. Many people wanted to hear what they had to say, including Nelly and her mother. Upon entering the church, the mother and daughter discovered that about two hundred people were attending prayer meeting that evening.

When it was time to begin the meeting, Brother James and Sister White walked right up to the front and sat on the lower platform. After a few songs, Brother White spoke for ten minutes and then said humbly, "I know you didn't come to hear me. You really want to hear my wife, so I'll let her speak now." So Sister White got up and spoke for about half an hour.

She spoke about her concern that many were not ready for Jesus to come and urged people to get ready for His soon coming. She told them that Adventists should be strangers in this world, but that some weren't preparing for the future life in heaven. Instead, they were too interested in the things of this world.

Suddenly, Sister White seemed to fall backward to the floor. But she didn't drop on the floor with a thud. It appeared to Nelly and her mother as if some unseen presence was gently lowering her to the carpet. Initially, the two of them thought that Sister White had fainted. They'd never seen her in vision before.

Miracles in Unexpected Places

Nelly had heard it was said around Battle Creek that when Sister White fell into vision, she shouted, "Glory!" or "Glory to God!" This time, she didn't. *It is not uncommon for women to faint,* Nelly thought to herself, and Sister White, at first glance, usually appeared weak and frail. Apparently, many others in the prayer meeting also thought that Sister White simply had fainted, for a few jumped up and opened the windows wider. Someone else brought Sister White a glass of water.

Brother White stood up and said, "Don't be alarmed. Sister White has not fainted. She's in vision." When the congregation heard Brother James say that his wife was in vision, a quietness came over them. Nelly thought that it was as if heavenly beings were present there in that church. No one appeared frightened. Sister White was lying on the lower platform, completely quiet and absolutely unconscious. Brother James continued, "There are some in this congregation who may have doubt in regards to Sister White's inspiration and about her visions. If there are any such, please come forward and try the physical tests as they are given in the Bible."

Then Brother White knelt down by his wife and raised her head and shoulders so that they rested on his knee.

Nelly knew that her mother had doubts about whether Sister White was a prophet, so she said, "Mother, why don't we go up and see Sister White up close as Brother White has invited us to do?" Her mother nodded, so the two of them went up front and stood very close to her head. They could see that she didn't breathe. Her eyes were open and there was a pleasant expression on her face. As far as Nelly could tell, Sister White looked quite natural, even though she didn't seem to be breathing.

Others came up, too, including two large men who worked at the sanitarium. One stood on either side of Sister White. Then Brother White spoke again, saying, "You've all seen my wife fall, revealing that she's lost her natural strength. Now see if she's been supernaturally strengthened." Her arms were clasped lightly against her chest. Brother White challenged the two large men, "I want you to pull Sister White's hands apart. You'll each have two hands to her one." Each of the men pulled one arm.

With both hands these large men pulled and pulled on the petite woman's arms, but nothing happened. Then they pulled even harder, but they still couldn't pull her arms apart. Nelly and some others became concerned that these men might hurt Sister White, but Brother James reassured them, "Don't be anxious. She's in God's keeping. You can pull all you want until you're satisfied."

The two large men responded, "We're satisfied now that Sister White has supernatural strength. We don't need to pull on her arms anymore."

Brother White said, "Take one finger at a time and try to pull them apart."

Once again they pulled and pulled, but her hand rested on her chest. They couldn't even lift one finger.

Despite all the distraction of the workers from the sanitarium pulling on Sister White's arms and the commentary from Brother White, Nelly kept her eyes on Sister White's face. She noted that at no time did her facial expression give any indication that she was aware of their presence.

After a while, Sister White on her own moved her arms apart and began gracefully gesturing with them.

Brother White said to the two large men, "Now I want you to hold her arms. See if you can keep her from moving them." The strong men took ahold of Sister White's wrists and tried to hold her arms still, but they couldn't. She moved her arms as if no one was holding them. Their initial fear that they might hurt her, or somehow interfere with whatever she might be seeing, evaporated when Brother White assured them that they couldn't hurt her. "You won't interfere with her vision in the slightest. Even though she's unconscious to anything around her, she's safe in God's hands," he added.

Nelly noticed something else about Sister White's expression. She wasn't blinking. Her eyelids never closed.

Brother White said, "Now that we are satisfied that her own strength is gone and that she has supernatural strength, let's see if her eyelids will close." On a stand nearby was a brightly burning lamp. Someone brought it to Brother White and, after he had removed the shade, he brought it close to his wife's eyes. Nelly cringed as he brought the bright lamp right in front of Sister White's eyes. Nelly felt certain that she would move her eyes to protect them, or close her eyes, but to Nelly's surprise, she didn't. Sister White seemed unaware of the bright light close to her eyes. Brother White took the lamp away and handed it to someone, who placed it back on the stand.

Nelly saw that Sister White's eyes weren't starry or glassy; however, from time to time, Nelly noticed that Sister White's expression changed. Fascinated, she watched her face. At times, Sister White looked pleased, but at other times she seemed troubled. Occasionally she spoke a short sentence, evidently about the things she was seeing in vision. At times her face seemed animated and excited. At other times, she seemed to shrink away from something she'd seen.

Brother White said, "Now let's see whether Sister White is breathing." Nelly had already noted that Sister White didn't seem to be breathing, but she reasoned that she could've been lightly breathing. She, her mother, and the others who were standing around Sister White wanted to know for sure. Brother White called for a mirror and someone ran from the church, borrowed one from the house next door, and returned with it.

Nelly thought Brother White had devised a good test. If his wife were indeed breathing, even slightly, the moisture from her breath would steam up the mirror. As Brother White held the mirror under his wife's nose, Nelly looked closely to see what would happen. The mirror didn't fog up. Those around her murmured among themselves that breath fogs up mirrors. Now Nelly and all the others on the platform knew for certain that Sister White definitely wasn't breathing. Someone reached down and felt Sister White's pulse and discovered that her heart continued to beat regularly. Everyone noted that the color in her face hadn't changed.

Eventually, Sister White came out of vision.

When she began to come out of vision, she took three long, deep breaths. Her lungs had been empty.

Her husband assisted her to a chair, then said to her, "The congregation would be very interested in your vision. I know that they will want to know something about what you've seen."

Sister White replied that she'd gladly tell the people what she'd seen in her vision. She stood quietly before the congregation for a moment, then explained. "My eyes need to adjust. It's so dark down here in this old world." She told the people, "If you turn your face toward the sun for a while, then turn away, you'll understand. Heaven is brighter than the sun." Gradually she regained the use of her sight. Nelly noted that the experience of being in vision didn't seem to injure her sight at all. Also Nelly could tell that once Sister White was out of vision, she didn't appear to be feeling weak or ill.

For about half an hour she talked. She said, "I saw the bright and glorious home God is preparing for his people." She'd also seen the destruction of the wicked. "I'm troubled that some of those destroyed were those who'd once been

Nelly's Fright and Ellen G. White

Seventh-day Adventists. They'd started on the narrow path, but had, for various reasons, turned aside. Some had become discouraged; others enjoyed the pleasures of this world too much. While still others," she said, "were too interested in making money."

When Sister White talked about the New Jerusalem, she said, "Oh I wish I could describe it. I have no language in which to tell you even a little of what has been shown to me. If you could be there and see what I saw, you'd never allow anything on this world to tempt you to live in such a way as to be in danger of losing eternal life."

Sister White then told the congregation, "It's not the large sins that we do, but the little things, like carelessness, or not fully accepting the responsibility that the Lord would place on us, that we need to be especially mindful of. We are living too lightly. We are spending too much time and thought on our present interests. Some of these things may be all right in themselves, but they crowd out the heavenly things. And, of course, the purpose of our temporary life on this earth is to secure eternal life in heaven."

When Nelly and her mother left prayer meeting that Friday, they were happy that they'd attended. They were glad that they'd had the opportunity to see Ellen G. White in vision. They said to each other, "We know that God gave her those visions, and we want to study her counsel and apply it to our everyday lives."

Ellen White later wrote down the complete vision. You can read it in *Testimonies to the Church,* volume 2, pages 112–199.

Nelly grew up to marry a minister and spent most of her life in America and Australia. While in Australia, she often traveled with Sister White. At times she and her husband even lived in Sister White's home. Truly, Nelly never forgot that night in Battle Creek, Michigan, on June 12, 1868, when she first saw Ellen G. White in vision. It convinced her that Sister White was indeed a prophet of God.

Chapter 21

The Mystery of the Missing Mashed Maize Patties

Isaiah and Solomon, a couple of traveling book salesmen, came to a village in Kenya, East Africa. As was their custom, they asked the village chief if they could stay overnight. The chief, who also happened to be the village witch doctor, gave his consent, saying, "I'll organize a welcome feast for you to introduce you to the village."

Feeling certain that the chief's welcome feast was a sign that God wanted them to work in the village, Isaiah and Solomon made plans to stay. That afternoon, true to his word, the witch doctor invited the villagers to a feast. After his announcement, he set up a large tent in the middle of the village, and the villagers began preparing the food.

Soon all was in readiness. The table was set with mashed maize patties, baked yams, and fruit. Dogs, with hungry looks in their eyes, mingled among the villagers. Indeed, as both the villagers and the dogs eyed the food on the table in the tent, it was difficult to tell who was more eager to devour it.

When the people were about to eat, the traveling salesmen, to the amazement of the villagers, rose from their chairs, knelt on the packed-mud floor, folded their hands, closed their eyes, and prayed aloud for God to bless the food. As Isaiah and Solomon were praying, all the villagers, out of politeness for their guests, followed Isaiah's and Solomon's example and closed their eyes.

The Mystery of the Missing Mashed Maize Patties

Yap! Yap! Yap!
Arf-arf-arf-ai-oooooo!
Grrruff! Grruff! Grrruff!
Yip! Yip! Yip! Yip! Yip!

When the prayer had ended and everyone opened their eyes, the villagers were surprised to see that all the dogs had left the tent and were standing outside, snarling, barking, and howling noisily.

The villagers and the traveling salesmen also noted that, while all the food remained on the villager's plates, the plates of the two salesmen were different. The yams and fruits remained on Isaiah's and Solomon's plates, but their maize patties had disappeared.

The two guests puzzled over the missing maize patties. But not wanting to embarrass their host, the chief, who was responsible for the feast in their honor, the two salesmen decided it was better to say nothing about the missing patties.

As Isaiah and Solomon ate their baked yams and fruits, the dogs outside the tent continued to yowl and whine loudly. *If they were still hungry for the food, why did the dogs leave? Are they fighting?* Solomon wondered. As disturbing as the canine growls, yelps, and howls were, the traveling salesmen ignored them. All in attendance at the feast listened intently as Isaiah and Solomon talked about the books and what they could teach about God.

After the meal, a few villagers bought books. Then Isaiah and Solomon announced that they had changed their plans and were going to move on to another village before nightfall. So they packed their books and left the village on foot.

Isaiah and Solomon were fast walkers, used to walking long distances and occasionally even trekking all night long. To stay awake, and keep furry predators at bay, they talked loudly to each other about anything they could think about.

"Quiet!" Solomon whispered as they walked.

"What?" asked Isaiah.

"Did you hear steps behind us?" They slowed a little and listened carefully.

"Something—" Solomon began.

"Or someone—" Isaiah interrupted as the booksellers' eyes met.

"Is following us!" they said in unison.

"It might be a lion," suggested Isaiah.

"Or worse," Solomon replied, "a tiger!"

"A tiger might be worse," Isaiah agreed. "Let's get out of this jungle." They quickened their pace.

So did the pursuer.

"It might be a thief!" Solomon suggested. The booksellers doubled their pace.

So did the hunter.

Soon it became evident that the stalker was too fast for them. Looking over their shoulders, the booksellers saw the face of the man who was chasing them. It was none other than the witch doctor who was also the chief from the village where they'd feasted.

A bit apprehensive about what the witch doctor might want, the booksellers stopped, allowing him to catch up. When the witch doctor had caught his breath, Solomon asked, "Is anything wrong?"

Isaiah asked, "Is there anything we can do to help you?"

Still gasping, the witch doctor managed to say, "I—don't—understand—it."

"What don't you understand?" asked Solomon patiently.

After taking a deep breath, the witch doctor tried to explain, "Do you remember when we were eating and the dogs were extra noisy?"

The booksellers nodded that they'd remembered. *How could we forget?* they thought to themselves. *We had to raise our voices over the sound of the dogs' howls, yips, and whines.*

"Well, now all the dogs are dead," the witch doctor announced.

"Oh, I'm so sorry to hear that," Solomon said sympathetically.

"Are the villagers upset?" Isaiah asked.

"Why did they die?" Solomon asked.

The witch doctor didn't reply. Instead he hung his head.

"Do you have any idea?" Isaiah coaxed.

"It's all my fault," the witch doctor finally admitted.

"How so?" Solomon asked.

"When you came to the village and asked to stay," the witch doctor explained, "I agreed."

The booksellers nodded.

"But actually, I planned to do you evil," the witch doctor continued. "I didn't want my people to read your books because I believed they were no good and that they might reduce my influence in the village. So when I organized the feast, I secretly fixed special maize patties for you."

"Really?" Solomon gasped.

"Yes," said the witch doctor. "In them I mixed in one of my famous potions—an extremely lethal one. I wanted you two dead! I planned that as you were talking about your books, you'd fall over dead, and the villagers would know better than to buy books like yours."

The two booksellers looked at each other nervously, wondering what the witch doctor would do or say next.

"It was a good plan. But before you ate," the witch doctor continued, "you prayed to your God, and the patties on your plates disappeared. And now all the dogs are dead." He paused as if to let the truth sink in.

"I don't know what truth you have," the witch doctor continued, "but whatever it is, I want to learn about it! Please teach me about your God!"

After hearing that appeal, the booksellers changed their plans. "Instead of continuing on to the next village tonight, we'll return to your village," they told the chief.

Happily, the witch doctor studied with the two book salesmen and became a Christian. Today he's still the leader of his village, but he's no longer the witch doctor. All of the villagers are Christian, and the village chief is also their respected church elder.

And to think that it all happened because of two traveling salesmen who said grace before eating.

However, it's still a mystery how the dogs got the patties. As all eyes were closed while the booksellers said grace; no one saw what happened. Did the dogs eat the patties from their plates while the salesmen prayed? If so, why didn't they also eat the yams and fruit?

Or did an unseen hand take the poisoned patties and place them outside the tent? If so, because all the dogs died, how did they all eat the patties? Did the dogs fight over them and each get a bite or two? If so, it must indeed have been a very lethal potion.

All I know is that God works in mysterious ways to reach His people. He can turn evil plans into good, for, as the scripture says, all things work together for good to those who love God.

Chapter 22

The Hapless Galapagos Lobster

Part 1: The Harsh Island Paradise

"Hey," I shouted, "that little bird just hopped on my plate and flew off with some of my food. The little thief!"

"I saw that! Darwin's finches are pretty bold and daring, aren't they?" laughed Daryl, a short-haired, freckled brunet science student whose father was a family doctor in Maine. "They're great opportunists 'cause they need to be to survive in the sometimes harsh environment of the Galapagos. You gotta admit though, they're fearless."

"Since that bird has walked on my plate," I bellyached, "I don't feel like eating anymore."

"I know what you mean," Daryl said, "but if you're still hungry, I don't think there'll be any more food 'til evening, so better eat up—at least from the other side of the plate where the bird didn't stand."

"I don't think I like Darwin's finches anymore."

"They're pretty drab, aren't they?" Daryl agreed. "They're just a dull brown. On the surface, they don't really look much different from the finches back home, do they?"

"And I really can't tell which beak is what," I said. "They're a lot smaller than I thought they'd be."

The Hapless Galapagos Lobster

"That last sentence hinted at some scientific observation while the rest was emotional." Daryl smiled encouragingly. "Don't forget, we're here to observe and learn from nature."

I nodded. "Maybe I'd like them more if one of them picked up a cactus needle and started using it."

"Was Darwin correct about the changes he reported seeing on these islands?" Daryl's eyes twinkled. "Or wasn't he?"

"That's the great question, isn't it?" I added.

"You know Darwin's finches are only found on Galapagos. So, start looking closely at those beaks and they'll help you see how animals' DNA can help the little birds change so they can live on these harsh islands," said Daryl, before he added mischievously, "if Darwin is correct, that is."

"Right," I said. "I just don't want to study those thieving beaks at lunchtime!"

"Lunch may be the best way to get finch beaks close enough for scrutiny," Daryl advised with a wry grin.

Just then, the director of the biological study tour, Professor Parris, stepped on to the porch and announced, "Pack your things; we're going to the harbor. We plan to study the unique plants and animals of the islands. As scientists, we'll reexamine the evolutionary laboratory that Charles Darwin described and test with our own eyes the validity of his ideas."

Daryl looked over at me and winked. I smiled, rolled my eyes, and mouthed, "I know, I know, finch beaks." We laughed together as the professor turned to go.

I went back into the station, placed a few items into my backpack, threw it over my shoulder, and waited outside. Soon we were all rattling down the road in a bus heading toward the harbor. At our destination, we stood around some benches along the waterfront as the professor made arrangements. Not a few of the benches were taken by Galapagos seals who, unafraid of the tourists and villagers milling around, lazed contentedly and barked at anyone who dared to try to share their benches.

The professor climbed off a boat on to the harbor and motioned for us to gather around him. When we were within earshot, he said, "We've booked two boats that will be our homes for the next two months. This year marks the centennial of the death of Charles Darwin, who also spent two months on a ship touring the islands. After we've completed our tour, we'll be about as qualified as he was to make conclusions about the biology of the creatures on this archipelago. My hypothesis is that we'll discover that what he saw was true, but we might argue with his conclusions. So, let me tell you which boats you're assigned to." The women and the married couples shared the boat with the professors, while the bachelors were assigned the other one.

"Before we climb aboard our ships, I want to talk to you about the food." Everyone stopped to listen. "When we're on these ships, we won't be able to stop at any restaurants because most of the islands are parks for wildlife. We'll need to eat whatever the crew prepares for us. I'm aware that some of you are vegetarians. I want everyone to eat whatever food is set before you. I don't want to hear anyone complain about being served meat. We've gotta be careful what we say to these hard-working crew members on our boats, or we might insult them. That wouldn't leave a good impression, would it?"

"Surely you're only talking about the clean meats, Prof," Chloe, a blue-eyed science student with long brown hair asked.

"Oh, no!" Professor Parris retorted. "I'm talking about all meat, clean or unclean. You can eat it here—even seafood—because it's a very clean environment out here in the Galapagos, not like back home in smoggy California. Even the scavengers are eating clean food here," the professor asserted, "so all the meat here is healthy. Does everyone understand?"

Some people mumbled among themselves, but no one spoke up.

"I'm afraid that someone may try to tell the cooks on these boats that their food is bad and hurt their feelings," the prof said. "I don't want anyone insulting them over the food just because of their diet."

The murmuring died down. The professor nodded his head and directed us toward the boats with his hand. "All aboard!"

Inside the boat, I sat contemplating the professor's words. He'd said he didn't want anyone *complaining* about meat being served because unkind words might insult the cooks. But that didn't mean I was obliged to eat meat.

When our boat left the harbor and sailed into the ocean, I began to have sympathy for Darwin, who was terribly seasick most of the time on board the *Beagle*. The oft violently choppy water tossed the boat mercilessly over the waves. Dramamine and I don't get along well during the day because of its drowsy side effects. Like Darwin, I spent time lying in my bed; but unlike him, I kept my eye on the porthole in an attempt to secure a semblance of equilibrium. Unlike

The Hapless Galapagos Lobster

Darwin, I soon gained my sea legs and learned to function onboard.

The crew dropped anchor at mealtime in quieter water and rang an orchestral triangle announcing that the food was ready. We congregated around the table and found seats. My fellow students hungrily served themselves. Jake, a green-eyed wavy-haired blond whose father operated a dentist's office in Southern California, served himself sausage and said to the others, "Don't forget what Prof said about eating what's set before you." Daniel said, "Pass the pork sausages, if that's what they are." He put three on his plate and began eating with relish. Others grabbed beef patties, vigorously cutting them with fork and knife, and eagerly devouring them.

Quietly, while the meat was rapidly disappearing, I served myself rice from one plate, beans from another, and vegetables from a third. As the rest competed for the meat, I helped myself to a second serving of rice and vegetables.

We disembarked and stepped gingerly on the rocky shore, trying not to step on marine iguanas that were soaking up the sun's heat on the hot lava rocks. Some were waddling along nonchalantly, completely devoid of fear. "Hey, dude, check this out!" a rather plump fellow named Caleb said as he reached out to stroke one.

"Awesome, totally awesome, dude!" said Justin, who, like Caleb, looked and sounded every bit the personification of a stereotypical surfer from California.

"Wouldn't one of these bodacious fellas look totally cool perched on one of my empty bookshelves back in my dorm?" Caleb said.

"Oh, dude, yeah, totally rad!" said Justin.

I lay on the lava rock and watched the lizards spit saltwater through their noses. I marveled at the miracle within their genes that allowed some iguana in the islands to be able to filter salt so they could feed in the sea. Almost as if they were on rotation, some of these cold-blooded creatures waddled down into the water for a dive.

On the boat at mealtime, I was again happy to see that our cooks had separated the food. Once again, the others students on the boat piled their plates with the meat, leaving the rice, beans, and vegetables, which I quietly selected.

A few hours later, we donned our swimsuits, climbed into the dinghy, rowed out to calmer water, and plunged in for a swim. Suddenly, four of the students shouted, "Sharks!" and literally jumped a few inches out of the sea. They began humming the theme from the movie *Jaws* as they raced for the dinghy and fairly leaped out of the water on to it.

Miracles in Unexpected Places

Looking down into the clear water below, I saw the bay sharks and hammerhead sharks that the others had feared and laughed. However, as they were about to row back to the ship, I swam over and joined them. "You know," I said calmly as I climbed in, "those aren't great whites down there. Bay sharks and hammerheads are pretty harmless—unless you're a fish."

They shook their heads in disbelief, saying that they were Californians and that I was from Michigan and pointed out the obvious fact that their great state had much more oceanfront than mine did, so who was I to talk? They calmed down a bit when I mentioned that my grandparents were from Central California and that I visited them every summer. Nevertheless, they insisted upon rowing back to the ship, where they related their side of the story to the other students. Their fright made everyone hungry, and they were happy when the next meal was served. Again, they ate the meat, while I ate vegetables, eggs, rice, and beans.

After the meal, as we sailed over open water, Caleb, the rotund member in the group, who was a bit of a showman, called us together, "Dudes, like I totally ate too much, man! Wouldn't it be totally rad to see how much seawater I can drink before I upchuck my meal all over the side?" Daryl, the New England Yankee from Maine, briefly pointed out the dangers of drinking seawater, but Caleb dismissed the objection with a casual wave of his hand. "No, dudes, it's totally not like I'm keeping the seawater in my body—that would never do. Understand?" As there was nothing much else to do on the boat, there were nods of assent as Justin and some of the others said, "Totally!"

Caleb urged us to pick a number, then he took his mug, reached over the side of the boat, filled it, and drank the seawater. He screwed up his face and declared it tasted dreadful. The count began, "One!" It continued until it reached nine. Suddenly, Caleb bent over the side and hurled everything overboard. Rising, he made a victory lap around the boat then sat at the table, indicating that the show was over.

The next day we were on shore watching the crazy antics of blue-footed boobies as the little clownish birds stumbled around their nests on their big, blue-webbed feet and displayed their affection for each other by clacking their bills together. Walking among the island's unique wildlife and seeing how they are fearless around humans gave me a feeling that, while I was on these enchanted Galapagos Islands, I was getting a little foretaste of heaven. I recalled

The Hapless Galapagos Lobster

seeing misty moss hanging from exotic plants and remembered half-expecting Sir Galahad and the knights of the Round Table to appear riding through the fog in an Arthurian legend. Or I imagined I might see the smile of a fading Cheshire cat beaming down at me from a cactus tree. Might a troop of hobbits or the Seven Dwarfs appear in some Tolkienlike fantasy? Then I reminded myself that, as fabulous as these impressions of "Alice's Wonderland in the Galapagos Islands" might be, heaven would be even more fantastic than this!

Back on the boat, the meal was served as before with the meat separate from the rest of the food. Again, I helped myself to vegetarian fare as the others eagerly grabbed up all the meat. I was feeling good that I'd been able to eat vegetarian every day on the boat without saying a word of complaint. I wondered how the vegetarians were faring on the other boat.

On land, I managed to take Chloe aside and ask her about the cooks on her boat. Earlier she'd objected most loudly about having to eat meat. The look on her face wasn't happy. "Our cooks serve meat in our rice and salads," she sounded dismayed and resigned. "Prof gives me a dirty look if I don't eat it. I suspect that when he made that unfortunate announcement, he was thinking about me, because he knows I'm quite vocal about my opinions." I gave her my sympathies.

The fear of sharks was downgraded to a healthy respect for them among the other students. Was it something I'd said about great whites and hammerheads? Fishing poles were set up on the daring hope of catching one. Day after day, the fishing line saw no action.

On land again, as I was walking down a trail, I encountered an old Galapagos tortoise, which may have even seen Charles Darwin himself. I sat on his shell and the ancient reptile gave me a ride for a few steps. Then we did our best to smile for the camera. Self-conscious, I hid my teeth, turning my smile into a grin; the tortoise had none to hide.

Back on the boat, riding the high seas, there was a tug on one of the fishing lines. Looking out at the sea, we saw that at the other end of the line was a bay shark. "Totally awesome, dude," exclaimed Justin and the others. "You caught 'im with just a fishhook, dude! That's totally gnarly! Dude, don't let 'im get away!" We all took turns keeping the line taunt until the great fish no longer resisted then reeled it on to the ship. "I want the jaw," said Jonathan, the rusty-haired dentist's son whose line had snagged it. Once it was certain that the great beast was dead, the jaw was removed and set out in the sun to dry.

On the next island Professor Parris proclaimed, "This is our last island. The boats will be taking us back to the biological station where you'll be writing about your biological adventure of exploring the incredible wildlife living here on these idyllic islands. You'll have been on the islands as long as Darwin himself; therefore, you'll be about as qualified as he was to make conclusions," he smiled conspiratorially. "Of course, if you have questions about the facts, we professors will be on hand to assist, but we'll be interested in how you defend your position. If Darwin was right, explain; if not, show us where he went astray in his conclusions."

That night I dreamed of the paper I would write. It was pretty amazing to see so many animals that are only found on the Galapagos Islands. They definitely didn't come there as they were now. While I'd seen iguanas adapt to eating underwater and cormorants evolve smaller wings, rendering them flightless, I'd never seen iguanas become blue-footed boobies, or tortoises become Galapagos penguins. There were quite a number of Darwin's finches with quite a variety of differences, but I reasoned that there was a simple solution to that problem.

Writing scientifically, I couldn't just say God loves His creatures so much He set up a code in their DNA that allows for change. No, miracles aren't considered scientific. I had a logical solution. I thought the problem was in the classifications system. If the annoying little finches were all placed at a subspecies level, they'd be merely varieties of the same bird.*

After we'd reached the highest point on the islands and pitched our tents for the night, Professor Parris announced, "While we hike this island, examining its unique vegetation and wildlife, the cooks will set lobster traps. We're in perhaps the world's cleanest waters right now, so these crustaceans are eating clean food. The crew will be very proud of their catch, so I don't want any of you to make them feel bad."

On the boat, the cooks proudly showed us the hapless lobster they had trapped. As there was a language barrier, the boat crew flexed their muscles in a show of man's victory over the wild. Then the crustacean was carried off brusquely to the kitchen. Someone joked that it would be the guest of honor at the next meal.

---

* For more on this, read Stanley Maxwell's "I Visited Darwin's Islands," *Signs of the Times*®, vol. 110 (November 1983), 4, 5.

The Hapless Galapagos Lobster

Soon the cooks jangled their percussionist's triangle, announcing that it was time to eat; I showed up with the rest.

There, in the center of the table, sitting on a tin serving plate, was a boiled lobster. Having had its outer shell removed, the whitish flesh somehow made it appear as though it were naked. Or was it a knight without armor? Unfortunately for me, this time the cooks had prepared no rice, beans, or vegetables. There was no sauce. Nothing else. Just a boiled lobster.

Unable to serve myself anything else, I remained in my seat at the table, saying nothing and taking no servings, hoping that no one would notice.

Part 2: The Lobster Tale

"You trippin' out or what, dude?" said Justin. "Don't think we ain't seen your empty plate. We care about you, man. While you're dreamin', the food is disappearin'. Dig in, man, 'fore it's all gone!"

I shook my head.

"What's the matter, dude?" Caleb asked. "Not feelin' well?"

"There's nothing I can eat," I tried to explain.

"There is seafood," Jake stated the obvious. "A whole lobster. Fresh. Caught today. You don't get fresh lobster every day!"

I shook my head again.

Looking around at those sitting at the table, I saw puzzlement in their eyes.

"I'm vegetarian," I announced.

My fellow students' eyes widened incredulously.

"Be careful," said Daryl. "Don't forget what Prof said about—"

"I'm not complaining about their food," I said quietly. "I was just hoping that if I didn't eat anything today, no one would notice."

"Obviously, that didn't work out very well for ya, did it?" said Daniel. "We noticed, man. If we did, most likely them cooks will too. Eat up!"

"I can't eat it," I insisted, folding my arms against my chest.

"It was never a problem for you before, man," said Jonathan.

"Yeah, why start now, dude?" said Caleb. "Stay cool with it, man!"

"I haven't eaten any meat on this trip yet," I declared.

"But you were eating with us!" exclaimed Daryl.

"True," I said as I placed my hand on the table. "I was eating, but while you were eating the meat, I was helping myself to the rice, beans, and vegetables."

"You were?" exclaimed Jake and Daniel. Not a few mouths dropped before several students echoed in amazement, "Dude!"

"We never knew!" said Daryl.

"Then it seems I succeeded in my plan," I said as I rubbed an itch on my cheek. "I respect Prof Parris completely—rumor has it he failed in his doctorate simply 'cause he declared to his professors that he was a Creation scientist, a notion they considered an oxymoron. That declaration took guts! As I want to be accepted for my lifestyle, I also think I should be accepting of others' ways of living. I don't want to make a fuss, 'cause I think the good prof was right. A ruckus would offend someone."

Jake and Daryl nodded their heads approvingly.

"I listened very carefully to Prof Parris's instructions about eating meat on the ship," I continued, seeing that I had everyone's attention now. "What I heard him say was that he didn't want the cooks to be offended. So I figured that if I quietly ate the vegetables while you ate the meat, all the food would disappear and the cooks would be happy."

Looking at me as if he were seeing me in a new light, Jonathan said, "We never noticed."

"That's good. It means that the cooks most likely didn't either." I sounded relieved.

"We thought you were eating the meat with us," said Jake honestly.

I paused and stared momentarily at the boiled lobster then looked at those sitting around the table. "I didn't mean to deceive any of you," I replied. "I just didn't want to make a fuss; yet, I had to maintain my standards and live by my conscience. The food was always provided on separate dishes, so I served myself what I wanted to eat—vegetarian, while you ate what you wanted—meat. As far as I was concerned, it worked out pretty well for me. You all had enough to eat, and so did I."

The students were silent for a while.

"So what are ya gonna do now, dude?" A wide grin spread across Caleb's face. "Seems like you gotta eat lobster today, man—if you don't wanna offend the cooks, that is."

I pursed my lips in thought. Caleb certainly had a point. I didn't want to offend the cooks.

"Why don't you eat meat?" asked Daryl.

The Hapless Galapagos Lobster

"Many reasons," I began. "When my father was in college, he, like you, took premed. Don't ask me why, but the biology department in his college placed a cat lab right before lunch, which meant my father was dissecting before eating."

"Grody!" interjected Caleb. "That's just simply nasty!" he growled.

"Gag me!" Justin wrinkled up his face as if he himself were about to vomit. "That's totally grody to the max."

"One day, the food on the menu was fried chicken," I continued. "Ironically, he had dissected fowls in the cat lab."

"Gross, dude!"

"Yeah, you know it," I said. "As my father was lifting a fried chicken wing to his mouth"—as I spoke I pretended to be lifting something toward my face—"before he could take a bite," I opened my mouth to illustrate, "his over-active mind began identifying the muscles and veins in the wing. Suddenly, he was no longer holding fried chicken, instead, to him, it was just a dead bird."

"Yuck!" exclaimed Daniel. "What happened?"

"He set it down and that was the last piece of meat he ever ate."

"After that experience, I can respect your father's decision to become a vegetarian, but you haven't told us why you're one."

"I can't stomach it. I'll vomit like Caleb if I eat meat."

"I'm not stickin' 'round for that, dude," Caleb waved his hand as he got up from the table.

"You just gotta remember what Prof said about the cooks." Daryl said as the others stood up to leave. "Take a bite and see what happens."

I wrinkled my brow.

"Whatcha got to lose? The worst thing is vomiting, right?" They went to other sections of the boat, leaving me alone with the cooked lobster.

The crew, each boasting a beaming smile, came into the room after the others had left and sat across from me at the table. My terrible Spanish, which was only slightly better than the cooks' English, wasn't good enough to explain. All I could think of to say with my limited Spanish was that I was no longer hungry, which, I reasoned, was at least partially true. After looking at that boiled lobster, it had indeed taken my appetite away. Then I said, "Caleb," and held my hand to my mouth and pretended to vomit into it. The cooks smiled, laughed, and repeated, "Caleb." They pretended to stick their fingers down their throats until they gagged and laughed again good-naturedly.

I pointed to myself, made motions with my hands in the air with an imaginary fork in my hand, stabbed some imaginary food, and stuffed the imaginary items into my mouth. Still miming, I quickly turned my head and pretended to spew.

The cooks laughed again, then, to my dismay, pointed to the boiled lobster, encouraging me to eat. Unfortunately, it seemed I'd failed to communicate with my little act. *Had they thought I was still talking about Caleb?* Again, the cooks gestured toward the lobster dish.

Solemnly, I nodded, picked up a real fork, helped myself to a section of lobster, and plopped it unceremoniously into my mouth. Chewing on it was something like chomping on rubber.

Immediately, I gagged.

The cooks' smiles evaporated.

Hastily, I dashed to the side of the boat, leaned overboard, and upchucked, returning more than just the lobster back to its home in the sea. A little queasy, I staggered back to the table to discover that the lobster dish had been removed. The cooks were smiling. "It's all right," they said in Spanish. "We understand." They pretended to gag and pointed to me.

While I'd had no audience watching me vomit the lobster—no one had said a word—it was obvious to me that everyone aboard the boat knew the story.

At breakfast the next morning, the cooks served bacon, boiled eggs, and sausages. Three of the passengers had already helped themselves to eggs. The rest had piled their plates with sausages and bacon. Hastily I snatched a couple of eggs before they were all gone. I cut an egg in half with my butter knife and began spooning the egg out of the shell.

"I've been doing a lot of thinking since last night," said Daryl. "I'm a vegetarian too."

"So am I," announced Jake, who was sitting directly across from me.

Daryl continued as he took a bite of egg, "And I didn't like eating the meat."

"Me too." Jake took his knife and cut his egg in half. "I like the way you eat eggs. Is this how you do it?" He took his spoon and began digging out the egg.

"I only ate meat because Prof said we might offend the cooks," Daryl explained as he peeled another egg and began mashing it until it looked scrambled.

"But you showed us another way," said Jake as he began spooning from the other half of the egg. "Thank you."

The Hapless Galapagos Lobster

For the rest of the trip, I was obliged to compete for my rice, beans, and veggies, but I didn't mind. By following my conscience throughout the trip and thanks to the boiled lobster incident, I felt like I was that proverbial pebble tossed into water, whose ripples soon spread across the entire lake.

Chapter 23

Jailbreak With God's Help!

As the paint sprayed from the can onto the office walls, Le Hoc Minh reflected. He'd been on the night shift spray-painting these same walls seven days a week for over a year. Ever since Saigon fell in 1975, the new regime had forced him to live in Cay Gua Reeducation Camp because he was a Nationalist Army veteran and a Protestant who had a locally famous parson—named Le Van Hien—for a grandfather.

Minh calculated how long he'd been in prison. The government had said it would be only six weeks, but as today was June 30, 1981, it had been six long years.

He'd been cultivating the trust of the Communists for several months and smiled to himself as he decided that they thought he and his team no longer wished to escape, preferring to await release. When weight loss had weakened him over a year before, the guards had mercifully placed him on the spray-painting crew.

Minh appreciated this transfer. Although spray-painting was boring and, he felt, wasteful of the country's resources, it beat cutting trees in the jungle and hauling them into camp every day. On that job, Minh had almost starved to death. The guards had expected him to bring in more logs every day, but each day they'd fed him less. But because he'd cooperated without a fuss, they'd begun to trust him.

He smiled again as he considered the guards' trust. Without their trust, he couldn't fulfill his plans for tonight.

Jailbreak With God's Help!

Tonight he planned to escape!

He reviewed his plans. He'd finish his shift, pretend to sleep in the office while team leader Sau slept and the third member of the work unit, Hong, took his shift spray-painting at midnight. That's when he'd begin his escape. Behind the office stood the prison wall. Minh planned to scale it and climb over the barbed-wire fence when Hong began painting on the other side of the office. No one was guarding the office, so he could climb the fence without being seen. The plan seemed so easy—perhaps too easy? Minh fretted impatiently as he watched Hong work.

He reviewed other inmates' escape attempts during the past year and a half. Twenty had failed. Only seven, maybe ten, had succeeded. One prisoner had been shot by guards as he'd tried to climb through the roof. Another tried to tunnel his way out, but a guard's foot sunk into the tunnel—only then had the hapless inmate discovered he'd been digging the wrong direction!

Would he succeed? If he didn't, he might be shot or placed back in the "white house." Minh had spent eight months in that white house. The guards had handcuffed him with his wrists touching each other, shackled his feet to a bar, and propped him up. Minh could only lie down or sit up and stare at the windowless whitewashed walls that had given the building its nickname. Four men had already tried to escape by climbing over the walls. They'd been recaptured and starved to death in the white house. Minh knew that death by bullet or starvation would be the reward for failure. But a prisoner's goal is to try to escape.

Minh thought of his almost-six-year-old daughter, Trang, whom he'd never seen. She lived at home with his wife. Every day he stayed in prison was another day his daughter would be raised by the Communists never to know God. This was his reason for climbing the prison walls.

At 2:00 A.M., Minh felt certain Sau had fallen sound asleep. He could hear Hong spraying and knew he couldn't see him. Sneaking from the office, Minh climbed the short fence to freedom. He stealthily and silently scrambled over the fence.

Once he'd successfully scaled the fence without being apprehended, Minh's impulse was to run away as fast as possible, but he knew that was foolish and would only guarantee his recapture. He must walk slowly, feeling the ground gently with his bare feet. Minh remembered from his tree-hauling days that, not far from the fence, arrows, partially buried in the ground, protruded spike-up to puncture the feet of any unsuspecting or panicking prisoner attempting to escape. If he were to catch his feet on the spikes, the guards and their dogs would follow his blood trail, and he'd soon be discovered. Minh's ultimate success depended upon his immediate dexterity. Slowing his pace, he cautiously progressed around the prison gate for the next four meters, trying to avoid the arrows.

Each step he took had to be soft enough so nothing sharp penetrated his skin. The starless, moonless night prevented the guards from seeing him, but the darkness also made it difficult for him to see where he was going. Minh didn't want to accidentally walk back toward the camp.

Once certain that he was successfully beyond the gate and thus free from the protruding arrows, Minh wiped his brow and took a deep breath. He knew that about a hundred meters from the camp lay National Route 4 to Ca Mau City. But, he asked himself, in which direction would he find it? No stars sparkled to guide him. Minh decided not to follow the road because if he did, it would be too easy to get caught. Traveling through the woods would be safer.

Once in the woods, he set out in the direction he assumed led to Route 4. Crouching behind a bush, he peaked through the leaves and saw a man riding a plow pulled by a water buffalo. Is the man a spy for the camp? Minh wondered. People in Vietnam plow fields around the clock, but Minh decided he couldn't risk exposure. Fearing the man might report him, he headed another way.

Knowing that he couldn't be too careful even though the night was dark, his heart raced as he imagined what might've happened had he entered the field without caution. Minh knelt and prayed. "God, help me! Send Your angel to go with me and keep me safe. I pray not for me, but for my daughter, Trang. I know You, but she cannot even sing a hymn. Lord, help me to escape with my family to Thailand so my daughter can learn to sing songs praising and glorifying You."

Reassured that God was his Guide, Minh swam across a stream about five hundred meters from the camp. Water helped disguise his trail. Being on the other side guaranteed he'd not accidentally walk into the soldier's quarters outside the reeducation camp; however, he must also carefully avoid stumbling into a smaller reeducation camp located near the Cay Gua Camp, where he'd once been held.

Jailbreak With God's Help!

Minh arrived at National Route 4 just as the sun rose. Darkness, his old friend, was receding into day. The road was dangerous now. If the guards were searching, he knew he could easily be seen. A river ran beside Route 4. Minh decided to cross it. Surely, the guards wouldn't search for him on the other side of the river. More likely they'd hunt him down along Route 4. Minh found a boat man and asked him to row him across.

"No," said the man. "But at the second house, there's a ferry. You wouldn't know it because there's no dock, but there's a little girl on the other side who'll ferry you across if you ask."

Uncertain whether or not to believe the man, Minh walked to the second house. Indeed it was just as the boat man had said. Nothing resembled a ferry station. There was no quay, no sampan, and no dock! Then he noticed a little girl about ten years old in a boat on the other shore. He signaled to her and she paddled across to meet him. He climbed aboard and she ferried him to the other side.

As the boat docked in its tiny harbor, which was so tiny it was hardly larger than the boat, Minh asked the girl, "How much?"

"Fifty cent," she replied. Reaching into his pocket, Minh took out some of the chump-change prisoners were paid that enabled them to buy from the prison guards' overpriced necessities, such as toothpaste and soap. Handing her one dong, twice the fare, Minh told her to keep the change, boarded the boat and tried to relax as she ferried him across.

After walking what he estimated to be about 1,200 meters, Minh felt that he was almost safe. Surely, Minh thought, God had helped him cross the river on a ferry no one could find without knowing the area. He believed God had heard his prayer and guided him to someone who'd informed him about that ferry. The South Vietnamese weren't cooperating with the new North Vietnamese regime. If the North Vietnamese prison guards asked for the ferry, Minh reasoned, probably the boatman wouldn't tell them where to find it. And if the guards knew where the ferry was, Minh reflected, the girl might not ferry them across or would take her time in coming to ferry them.

Minh now disguised himself as a farmer. Rolling up his right pant leg, securing a straw hat on his head, patching his clothes from scraps of material in his pockets, he began walking down the road, swinging his left arm wildly. Singing a Communist song—one that he'd helped rewrite while in reeducation camp—he hoped anyone who saw him would think him a supporter of the new regime and not a Nationalist veteran and Protestant who'd escaped from a reeducation camp. He thanked God for answering his prayers thus far.

The rest of Minh's escape story to his home on the South Vietnamese coast took many turns. But, eventually he was reunited with his family, and together they fled Vietnam by boat to Thailand. I met Minh three years later in Panat Nikhom Refugee Processing and Transit Center, near the village of KokPo in Thailand, where, at the time, I was teaching drama, English, and Western culture. He and his daughter, Trang, joined my church in the camp. Trang learned religious songs in my children's choir.

Minh believes God did indeed answer the prayer of an earnest father for his little daughter. Happily, Minh and his family were accepted for resettlement in North Carolina. Today, in his new homeland in America, Minh rejoices that his daughter loves God and sings His praises.

Chapter 24

Rat Poison to the Rescue!

How Samson Lionslayer got his name is quite a story. It wasn't the name given to him at birth. He earned his name partially through manhood rituals that his seminomadic tribe, the Maasai of Kenya, East Africa, required of the boys in the transition to adulthood.

When he reached his teens, Samson, along with other teens of the tribe, came to the manhood ceremony and stood at attention. The village elders positioned themselves a sword's length away from the youth, extended their swords toward the teens and with the point, extracted their lower two front teeth.

Why was this done even though the Kenyan government had outlawed such rituals? The answer can be given in three words: Tradition dies hard.

During this tooth-removing ritual, Samson was expected to show he was fearless by not yelling, crying, or wincing as his teeth were cut out by the sword. If successful, the boys were declared men because they'd shown courage.

In the next ritual, to show bravery, the young teen was required to hunt down a lion on his own and return wearing its skin. It was after he'd successfully accomplished that task that he assumed the name Lionslayer.

Lionslayer chose the name Samson after he became a Christian. When he told me this story, he claimed that he was the only Christian Red Maasai in Kenya. He explained that he'd named himself after Samson because the Bible character had slain a lion with his bare hands.

Once Jesus lived in his heart, Samson left his tribe and began traveling from village to village in Kenya, teaching others what he'd learned. In one Kenyan town where he was holding meetings, he met members of a Protestant church called the Reformed Church of East Africa.

Samson lectured about the Bible and Jesus. One of the pastors of the Reformed Church of East Africa attended the meetings. Taking Samson aside after one of the meetings, this pastor reached out his hand to shake Samson's and said, "Congratulations, Pastor Lionslayer! You've explained some parts of the Bible that I never understood before. It's all clear to me now."

"Praise God!" Samson exclaimed as he shook the pastor's hand. Elated that his lectures had reached a prominent member in the village, Samson hoped this pastor's influence would spread to others.

"I want to know more about what you believe," the pastor continued.

Faithfully, the pastor attended the lectures. In time, he asked Samson what he needed to do to join his church. Samson told him, "After you understand the Bible studies, you just need to be baptized."

Soon the date was set for the baptism. "I want to throw a feast for you on that day," the pastor told Samson excitedly. "We'll invite everyone in the town," he said. "I want the villagers to know about my new life with Jesus."

"That's a wonderful plan," Samson agreed.

Preparations for the meal were made well in advance. In fact, it took two days just to prepare all the food. All the leaders of the Reformed Church of East Africa and Samson were there to prepare the food.

When the food was prepared, everyone in the town came to the feast. Samson, as guest lecturer, was given a place of honor, along with the leaders of the Reformed Church of East Africa. After the food was formally blessed, everyone began to eat. The food was delicious.

Suddenly, some of the people at the feast came down with diarrhea. Others collapsed in their seats. Still others fainted. The only one at the feast who was not sick was Samson.

Seeing so many sick around him, Samson instinctively left his seat and came to their assistance. Suspecting something might be wrong with the food and fearing a plot was afoot, Samson called for a doctor. While he was awaiting him, Samson helped some of the weaker ones lie down and made sure they felt more comfortable.

When the doctor arrived, he began giving blood tests.

Rat Poison to the Rescue!

Soon the doctor returned, announcing, "The results of the tests are revealing that everyone here has blood poisoning."

"Do you have any idea what caused it?" Samson asked.

"It is clearly coming from Rat Run Away." Those at the feast knew that Rat Run Away was a local Kenyan brand of rat poison that was highly potent. "As I am suspecting foul play here," the doctor continued, "I've already notified the police. They've promised me they'll be investigating here soon and have informed me to say to all of you here that no one is permitted to leave the village."

When the police arrived, they began interrogating the villagers. After a while the police announced to the village, "This man confessed that he sneaked in the night before the feast and stirred rat poison into the food." Needless to say, this admission caused quite a stir among the villagers because the man who had poisoned the food was a member of the Reformed Church of East Africa.

Continuing their investigation in earnest, the police asked the suspect, "You say you mixed rat poison into the food last night."

Unable to meet anyone's eyes, the suspect hung his head.

"Why would you do this?" the police asked.

The suspect shook his head dejectedly.

"Were you angry at someone?"

Nervously flitting his eyes in the direction of an elder, then staring past the officer, the suspect looked as if he wanted to speak. Then, perhaps thinking better of it, he looked back down at the ground again and shook his head but said nothing.

"You weren't acting alone!" the police prodded.

Shuffling his feet slightly, the suspect made no other response.

"Someone put you up to it," the officer asserted. Standing closer to the suspect, he demanded, "Look at me when I'm speaking to you!"

Reluctantly the suspect obeyed, raising his head.

"You didn't think this through!" the officer asserted.

The suspect looked away.

"Keep your eyes on me!"

The suspect complied.

"This wasn't your idea, was it?" The officer's tone sounded warmer. The suspect shook his head again. "Who's behind this? Why should you take all the shame? It will go easier for you if you talk. Do you want to take his punishment for him?"

Silence.

"Who are you protecting!" the officer demanded. "Tell us!"

Buckling under the pressure, the suspect whispered, "I was given authorization."

Some of the villagers' eyes grew big.

"Thank you, my friend," smiled the officer gratefully. "Good for you. You made the right choice. Now we're getting somewhere. Things will go better for you now, my friend."

The suspect seemed to relax a little.

"Who was it?"

"A pastor." The suspect's words were barely audible.

"I can't hear you," the officer said. "Who was it?" He stepped closer to the suspect, who repeated his answer softly. "Who authorized you, my friend?" the officer continued kindly. "It'll go well for you if you help. Can you point him out to me?"

The suspect reluctantly pointed to the pastors of the Reformed Church of East Africa, "Talk to them. I don't know much."

Now many villagers' mouths dropped open. One or two gasped. Some villagers murmured.

The officer took the pastors aside and interviewed each one separately, then returned to the villagers. Confidently, the officer announced, "We've solved the mystery!"

The villagers were eager to listen.

Standing beside the church leader, the inspector explained, "Your pastors have confessed that the leader called them together and plotted with them to stir rat poison into the food to discredit your guest, Samson Lionslayer, who's been giving you Bible lectures. They thought that if all of you in the village got sick while eating with Samson, you'd determine that God was displeased with his teachings and you'd reject him and his message."

Abuzz with disbelief, the incredulous villagers challenged the inspector, "Why would our pastors do this to us?"

"Fear," the inspector explained.

"Fear?" the villagers echoed skeptically. "Of what?"

"I'm glad you asked," the inspector smiled. "I asked the very same question."

"And what did you learn?" the dubious villagers demanded.

148

Rat Poison to the Rescue!

Smugly, the officer explained, "Your pastors told me that their leader feared he'd lose his position of leadership in the village to Samson! And that they were afraid of your church leader."

Outrage exploded among most of the villagers, while others erupted with incredulity. After the hubbub died down, one of the skeptical ones shouted at the officer, "What methods did you use to extract this confession from our pastors?"

"We think you arrived at this conclusion too easily," stated another of the cynical villagers. "Haven't you forgotten something?"

"I think the mystery's been solved." The inspector then asked, "What've I missed?"

"What about Samson, himself?" The villagers declared, "Lionslayer's the only one who didn't get sick after eating at our feast. We think he poisoned the food!"

While the inspector rubbed his chin with apparent indecision, anger stirred the villagers into a frenzied crowd. "Did you consider that?" they taunted, "Why don't you interrogate our guest?" Some in the rowdy crowd chanted, "He's guilty! Samson's guilty!"

Just then Samson raised his hands. Perhaps because they were expecting a confession, the crowd calmed. When it was quiet, their guest spoke, "Please check the records. Don't forget my blood was tested too." Looking the villagers in the eye, he assured them, saying, "I ate the same food you did. Let's see if the test results show that I, too, have rat poison in my system."

The inspector quickly responded, "We'll check the records." He left to locate the doctor.

Satisfied that their demands were being considered, the villagers waited, expecting that Samson's deviousness would be discovered. Lionslayer overheard some of them whispering among themselves that, if their guest were guilty, his message must be from the devil. "We should run the scoundrel out of town and forget everything he taught."

Soon the doctor returned with the inspector and stood beside him. Eagerly, the villagers anticipated the verdict. Clearing his throat, the inspector solemnly announced, "Samson's blood-stream shows that he was indeed poisoned. Amazingly, however, the Rat Run Away did not make him sick."

Hearing this news, the attitude of the villagers altered. "It's a sign from God!" exclaimed some.

"It's a miracle!" others shouted.

"Samson's God is with him!" chimed in some more villagers.

"What he said about his blood system was correct, so what he says about God must be true as well," someone deducted. "That means we can believe what he says about the Bible."

Convinced that Samson was indeed sent from God, all of the pastors joined in with the villagers as they marveled at the way that God had protected Samson from the church leader's evil plan. They recalled that when every one of the villagers was sick, Samson had come to their aid. Immediately, the pastors proceeded to the doors of their church and locked them, ceremoniously announcing with dancing and song that the doors would never be reopened. "By locking the doors of the Reformed Church of East Africa," the pastors pledged, "we've symbolically locked the door on the past and set out for the bright future Samson the Lionslayer has revealed to us."

Indeed those doors were never again opened. Only one person in the village stubbornly refused to believe Samson was sent from God. The church leader refused to repent of his wicked plot to poison the village. So ashamed was he that his devious scheme to expose Samson as a fraud had backfired that he fled, never again to be seen in the village. Sadly, his worst fears had indeed come true. By his own willful choice, he lost his position as church leader in his village.

Samson Lionslayer later told me that everyone in the village helped to build a new church. The remaining pastors are now the leaders in this church, and all the villagers are faithful to what they learned from Samson.

It is amazing how God works when you're fighting His battles. When the church leader thought he'd be able to discredit Samson Lionslayer, and when the villagers were considering exiling him as a villain, it was, to everyone's surprise, rat poison that rescued him!

Samson concluded that the devil takes it upon himself to foil God's work; however, the Christian has no need to fear, because God can use anything to His advantage—even a generous dose of rat poison!

Chapter 25

The Mysterious Inn
by the Bridge

Part 1: A Son for Sale

In the days when the Empress Dowager ruled imperial China during the Ch'ing Dynasty and when women bound their feet tightly to keep their feet small, and men wore long braided ponytails called Manchu queues, an American nurse named Earnest Lutz* and his wife, Lillian, boarded a boat from the West Coast of the United States and eventually docked at the British harbor of Hong Kong off the coast of Canton Province.

Learning the language was Earnest's first priority. He and his wife determined to speak English at home only two days a week; the other five days they would speak only the local Chinese language. Soon Earnest felt confident enough to talk to people about Jesus. He was even willing to risk preaching a sermon. Hoping to be better able to reach the Chinese, he wanted to look and act as Chinese as possible. Being only five-foot-two, there was one thing he deeply appreciated about the Chinese; they were a people whom he could look squarely in the eye while in conversation, without craning his neck like he'd been forced to do in his native America.

After donning loose-fitting silk-and-cotton Chinese attire and braiding his hair in a traditional Manchu queue, Earnest walked to his destination in

---

* Lutz is pronounced *loots* and rhymes with *boots*.

Miracles in Unexpected Places

Canton Province where arrangements had been made for him to preach about Jesus. Upon his arrival, he was happy to see a group waiting. Eager to tell the people about what Jesus was doing for them in heaven, he spoke about the heavenly sanctuary. As the sermon progressed, Earnest rejoiced that the people were listening well and apparently could understand his message.

The attitude changed when he mentioned that Jesus went into the Most Holy Place from the Holy Place. Tittering ran through the congregation. As Earnest continued, the tittering grew into laughter. Thinking that the audience was disinterested, distracted—or worse, irreverent—Earnest struggled on.

Eventually, Mr. Lutz ended the sermon and proceeded to the back of the hall where he was greeted by the attendees. One old man who could speak English whispered into his ear, "Do you know why everyone laughed, honorable sir?"

Earnest admitted he didn't. "What was so funny?" Earnest asked.

"I know something about Bible, honorable sir. That why I understand what you want to say," the old man began to explain. "Other people in village not understand Bible like I do." He paused.

"Was it something I said?" Earnest had a sinking feeling.

"You talk about Holy Place and what your God Jesus already do there for everybody. I understand that you want to say 'Holy Place,' honorable sir."

"What did I actually say?" Earnest asked.

"I know you not know. That why I tell you, honorable sir." The old man smiled. "Chinese people call Holy Place *shun dee*, but you say *shu dee*. *Shu dee* not Holy Place; it poop place!"

"You mean I said Jesus did all those things in the bathroom?" Earnest blushed deeply.

"So sorry to say so, honorable sir," replied the old man politely.

Earnest couldn't help laughing. "No, you're right; I wasn't talking about what Jesus did in the bathroom. No wonder people laughed."

"Many think it so funny, honorable sir." The old man covered his mouth with his hand, and Earnest knew the old man was hiding mirth that, out of respect, he dared not show.

"I don't want to make that mistake again," Earnest said.

"Not many call bathroom by name *shu dee*. You speak Chinese language very well already for a *gwai-lo*." It was a backhanded compliment meaning foreigners can never learn Chinese like a native speaker, but that Earnest was doing very well. "Not to worry, honorable sir, people understand you say Jesus love us already before we love Him. You say Jesus take care of everybody and He come again," the old man reassured.

"Thank you," Earnest said, marveling to himself that God had blessed his message despite his blunder about Jesus' work in the sanctuary.

"I go already, honorable sir," the old man said. "Many people already waiting."

"Goodbye," Earnest said. "Always remember, God will take care of you."

"Bye-bye," the old man replied warmly. "I not forget what you say already." And he was gone.

It wasn't uncommon for Earnest to walk more than thirty miles in a day to share his love for Jesus with Chinese who wanted to listen to his messages. His daily journeys took him from Canton Province to an area near Chongqing where, when he arrived, he was overjoyed to learn that no one had ever seen someone from outside of China before. Noticing a commotion among a crowd of peasants, Earnest joined them.

"What's happening?" he asked.

"This farmer no can pay so much money owed, so he auction off Number One Son to pay back so many people," a peasant explained.

"Oh, the poor son," Earnest exclaimed. "What's to become of him?"

"He agree already to work forever for highest bidder," the peasant replied.

"So the son becomes a slave?" Earnest was aghast.

"The son agree to his father's plan already." The peasant, eager to bid, was now sounding impatient.

"What son in China would disagree?" Earnest thought aloud. "And the father will lose his firstborn son?" He felt his blood start to boil. "Who'll help the father on the rice paddies?"

"No time to talk," the peasant snapped and, holding up some money, shouted out a higher bid. Turning to Earnest, he snapped, "No money, no talk."

While Earnest was wishing he could somehow put a stop to the auction, the bidding war escalated as peasants shouted offers. While the boy stood stoically, his father's smile spread wider as the bids climbed rapidly.

Upset that a father was about to lose a valuable farm hand, Earnest longed to help. Suddenly the idea of an enacted parable struck him. Energetically, he began bidding. Instantly, the bid amounts skyrocketed. The frenzied competition soon ground to a halt, however, when Earnest offered an astronomical bid. Moments later, he was declared the winner.

Counting the money out, Earnest handed it to the beaming father, who hid the money in the folds of his clothes.

Walking tall and proud, Number One Son approached Earnest a few minutes later and kowtowed. "I work for you now, honorable sir," the boy said confidently from his prostrated position. "I big and strong—I work hard in rice field. What you want do now? I do anything you say."

"Stand up," Earnest said, "and dust off your clothes."

Number One Son dutifully obeyed.

Never once thinking that a father who'd auctioned off his son into slavery once might, in a financial pinch, decide to do it again, Earnest said, "Do this for me. I want you to go back to your father and work for him. Help him in the rice paddies."

"Don't you want me to work for you? I not good enough?" The boy looked bewildered.

"No, it's not that," Earnest began to explain his enacted parable.

"What?" the boy persisted.

"I bought you to set you *free*!"

Puzzled, the boy said, "You pay high price for me already. I work for you forever now. What do you mean 'free'?"

Earnest smiled kindly at the boy. "It's like what Jesus, the Son of God, did for us long ago."

"What do He do already?"

"Back in the beginning, our first parents, Adam and Eve, became slaves to Satan, the enemy of God; Jesus came here and paid an astronomically high price to buy us all so that He could set us free. Now, thanks to Him, we are all free indeed."

"That why you buy me and set me free?"

Earnest continued, "Yes, I want to teach you about freedom in Jesus. So I bought you, like He bought us, and set you free."

"Thank you, honorable sir." The boy bowed to Earnest.

"You're welcome," Earnest replied. "Now go back to your father. Tell him you're free to help him again."

"I go back; my father angry already." The boy sounded afraid. "You must explain what you want, nuh?"

"Sure!" Earnest agreed.

Earnest took Number One Son back to his father and explained. "Jesus set you free," he concluded. "Please tell this story to everyone you know."

"I say this story to many people, honorable sir. And story you tell about Jesus," Number One Son promised.

"God will be with you. He'll take care of you," Earnest said. "Never forget that."

"I promise," the father said.

"I never forget you and what you do today," Number One Son added.

Part 2: The Vanishing Inn

Happy that he'd had an opportunity to leave what he hoped was a lasting memory among the peasants near Chongqing, Earnest Lutz and his family, which now included two young sons, joined some American friends. Together, they continued trekking across China. One of their journeys took them from their headquarters in Chongqing to the countryside near Sichuan, where residents of a nearby jungle village wanted Earnest to talk to them about Jesus.

When the group started toward the jungle, friends in Sichuan urged, "Don't go now, it's too late."

"Why can't we go now?" Earnest asked.

"It's not safe," the friends advised.

"Why not?" Earnest wanted to know.

"Bandits! Lots of them," their friends exclaimed.

"What about bandits?"

"They live in the jungle and they'll rob you, maybe kill you," they explained. "You need to wait and start out early in the morning."

"But we won't get there in time," Earnest said. "We must leave now. Don't worry; God will be with us on our journey." Earnest and his family lit Chinese paper lanterns as they prepared to leave.

"Why are you taking those lanterns?" their friends asked. "You'll attract too much attention to yourselves."

"God will take care of us," Earnest reminded them with a smile.

"Using those lanterns is like shouting to the bandits, 'Here we are; attack us!' "

"The light from these paper lanterns will keep us from stumbling. Don't worry," Earnest assured them. "God will protect us from bandits."

Try as they might, their friends couldn't dissuade the Lutz family and the party from their plans. As the family started off, their lanterns formed dots of light along the trail. Porters carried Earnest's wife, Lillian, in a canopied sedan chair, but when the company reached the mountainous trail, she felt uneasy whenever the chair wobbled. "Please," Lillian begged the porters, "let me down. I'd rather walk." While she hiked the trail on foot, the puzzled porters dutifully followed, bearing an empty chair.

As the night grew darker, the travelers' feet grew wearier. The necessity of reaching their destination drove the determined party on. Stomachs rumbled, protesting that they were empty.

"I'm hungry," Earnest's elder son announced.

"So am I," his younger son concurred.

"We'll look for a good place to stop and eat," Earnest promised. While the answer quieted the boys, their tummies still complained.

Not long afterward, the party came to a bridge. "Look, there's an inn up ahead!"

"Do we have enough time to stop and eat there?" asked Lillian. Earnest decided that they did. Opening the door, they stepped inside.

Seeing his foreign guests kowtowing formally to him, the innkeeper urged them to rise. "Ah, welcome, most honorable sir. Please stay and dine."

"You have such a lovely establishment here, kind sir. We'll gladly dine here," Earnest said as he and his party rose from the floor.

"How soon can the food be ready, kind sir?" queried Lillian.

"I hope you understand if we don't stay long; we have a long way to go yet tonight," Earnest added.

"Ah, most honorable sir, and most honorable lady." The innkeeper smiled broadly as he bowed his head respectfully. "When I see many lantern in the distance come toward my honorable house, I think, guest plenty hungry already when they come to my humble inn. So I say already to honorable cook, 'Prepare really good meal for most honorable guest.' "

"So the food's ready now?" Lillian asked.

"Today, I give food, on the honorable house!" Extending his arm, the innkeeper pointed. "This way, honorable sir, an' honorable lady!" He led his guests into the dining area and showed them a table covered with a white cloth. Atop it were blue-and-white porcelain teacups and saucers and bowls. "You sit at table, and food coming already."

"Why thank you, kind sir," Earnest said gratefully.

"All for you, most honorable guest! What you want you say me." The innkeeper pointed to his nose. "I do what I can for you. I take care you, *la?*" With much fanfare, the innkeeper turned and grandly proceeded to the kitchen. The Lutzes and their party heard the innkeeper loudly admonishing his cook, "*Qwai diar!* (Hurry now!) *Eedien qwai!* (A little more quickly now!)"

Soon the food arrived, followed by another course and yet another. When his guests were satisfied, the innkeeper approached the table. "Please, you must stay today in my honorable house."

"Oh, kind sir, the food was so good," Earnest said. "I wish we could sleep here tonight."

"Ah, good, I most happy you decide already to stay," the innkeeper said.

"Oh, I'm so sorry, kind sir," Earnest gently replied, "but we can't possibly stay the night." Seeing disappointment cloud the innkeeper's face, Earnest quickly tried to explain, "We must reach our destination before morning."

"Where you going?" the innkeeper inquired.

Earnest Lutz told him.

"That far!" the innkeeper exclaimed incredulously. "You must stay in my honorable house."

"We have an appointment, kind sir, which we must keep."

"What appointment so important you risk life already, when you can sleep safe here tonight?" It wasn't really a question.

"God has taken care of us so far," Earnest said. "We are doing His work, so we know He'll protect us on our journey."

"Many bandit wait you tonight, honorable sir. You must stay. I prepare already your room here on the honorable house," the innkeeper insisted. "I take care you, honorable sir."

"We must continue our journey," Earnest maintained. "God will take care of us."

"Please, honorable sir, I keep you safe here!" The innkeeper was insistent. "Come see room I have already. I think you like, nuh?"

Reluctantly, Earnest and his company followed the innkeeper to see the rooms arranged for them.

"You sleep here tonight on the honorable house," persisted the innkeeper.

Seeing all the work that had been done in preparation for his arrival, Earnest didn't have the heart to refuse. That night the Lutz family and the rest of their party slept soundly. In the morning, the innkeeper served them a scrumptious breakfast before sending them on their way across the bridge toward the village.

Upon his arrival at their planned destination, Earnest discovered the villagers were anxiously awaiting them. "What take so long already?" they asked. "We want find you, honorable sir, but have no way! It is impossible. We fear already that many bandit capture you."

"God took care of us. We traveled into the night without seeing any bandits," Earnest explained. "Then we slept in the inn down the trail."

"What inn?" the villagers asked incredulously.

Astonished, Earnest answered, "The inn by the bridge."

"No inn exist by any bridge," the villagers retorted confidently.

"We were served two good meals there," Earnest protested. "And we spent the night in an inn by the bridge between here and Sichuan."

"Impossible!" The villagers shook their heads. Earnest knew that as far as the villagers were concerned, further discussion about the inn was fruitless. Knowing better than to say anything more aloud, Earnest thought to himself: *I know I ate and slept in an inn by the bridge, but the villagers say that what I experienced is impossible. Does the claim that no inn exists by the bridge mean that there really isn't one there, or does it mean that there is an inn located by the bridge, but that the villagers themselves never patronize it—which merely means that they don't recognize its existence?* He determined to solve this mystery on their return trip.

Eagerly, the villagers led Earnest and his company to where his meetings would take place and showed him where they'd be staying. During the meetings, some of the people liked what Earnest taught them about Jesus and the Bible.

Once the meetings were over, Earnest and his group prepared for their trek back to his Chongqing headquarters. From the elders, he learned that there were only two paths leading to the village—of those, only one led to Sichuan. Happily, he and his company retraced their steps, looking for the inn.

Arriving at the bridge, they were amazed to discover that there was nothing but jungle! Not only was there no inn, search as they might, the company could find no evidence that an inn had ever been built on either side of the bridge. Yet they all knew without a doubt that they had indeed dined and slept in an inn by that very bridge. Where was it? Where were the innkeeper and the cook? Nobody knew.

Were the innkeeper and the cook guardian angels? Did they build the inn? Where did it go?

Being unable to answer those questions themselves, the Lutz family came to this conclusion: God was with them on their journey through the jungle filled with bandits. He took care of them!

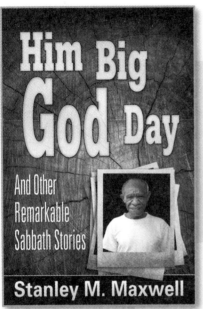

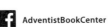